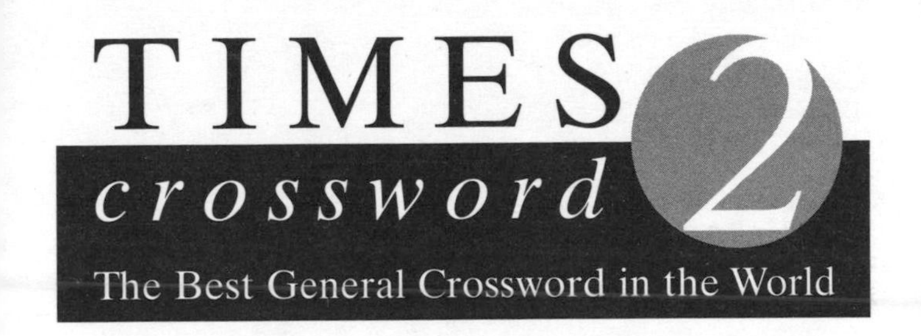

BOOK 3

Edited and introduced by
Richard Browne

TIMES BOOKS

This edition published 2010
First published in 2002 by Times Books as
The Times 2 Crossword Book 3

HarperCollins*Publishers*
77–85 Fulham Palace Road
Hammersmith
London W6 8JB

www.collins.co.uk

1

ISBN 9780007885732

A catalogue record for this book is available from the British Library.

Typeset in Great Britain by
Davidson Pre-Press Graphics Ltd, Glasgow G3

Printed and bound in Great Britain by
Clays Ltd, Suffolk

INTRODUCTION

Here is another selection of puzzles from the *Times 2* series, which appeared in *The Times* during the later months of 1998. They are reproduced here exactly as they appeared in the newspaper, except that some of the clues have been lengthened slightly, to take advantage of the extra space available in book form, and a few small changes have been made to eliminate repetitions of clues and answers, which pass without notice at a few months' distance in the daily sequence, but are not appropriate in a collection.

These puzzles are clued with definitions only, all trickery and deception being left firmly to our elder sibling, still known as *"The" Times* Crossword, although there has been this other one in one form or another now for nearly twenty years. Solving them calls for a reasonable amount of general knowledge, although I limit carefully what I put in, in two ways: first, I put in nothing that I do not know myself already (even if I have to check it – a process that regularly reveals that I don't know as much as I think I do). Second, I expect that many solvers will be tackling these puzzles in the train on the way to work, or in coffee breaks at it, where there is no ready recourse to reference books. Some solvers have told me that they do the crossword first thing in the morning in bed, to check whether they have enough brain left for it to be worth getting up. I would not like to think I am contributing to any discouragement!

Although these puzzles are all straightforward in their cluing, regular solvers will know that I occasionally add a little extra to them, in the form of hidden words or patterns, or connections suggested by the date or the puzzle number.

Noticing these is never necessary to the solution; but you may be interested to look out for these. (They are not in every puzzle.) In this context, I would mention that puzzle 14 was originally number 1492 and puzzle 74 number 1588; that puzzle 18 appeared as number 1500, and that the last puzzle appeared on Christmas Eve.

Richard Browne
Times 2 Editor

THE PUZZLES

ACROSS

1 Knocks off (e.g. pedestal) (7)

5 Royal golfcourse near Ayr (5)

8 (Mountain) crest (5)

9 Member of periodic table (7)

10 A game; horse-trials venue (9)

12 Debtor's note (1,1,1)

13 Sang under breath; (place) was busy (6)

14 Outskirts; short hair over brow (6)

17 Boy child (3)

18 Cleanshaven (9)

20 Volcanic (rock) (7)

21 Viper (5)

23 Horse (*poet.*) (5)

24 A fertiliser; sounds like *off-peak charge* (7)

DOWN

1 Pulsate (5)

2 Doctorate (*abbr.*) (2,1)

3 Sheltered half (of ship) (3,4)

4 Half rains half snows (6)

5 Coordinate (e.g. book with TV series) (3,2)

6 Compliance (9)

7 Japanese carved ivory (7)

11 Exercise of ascendancy (9)

13 Important person's jocular title (3,4)

15 Wholly change (document) (7)

16 Relay; die (4,2)

18 Fairhaired (man) (5)

19 Loose-stone slope (5)

22 Genetic-info molecule (*abbr.*) (1,1,1)

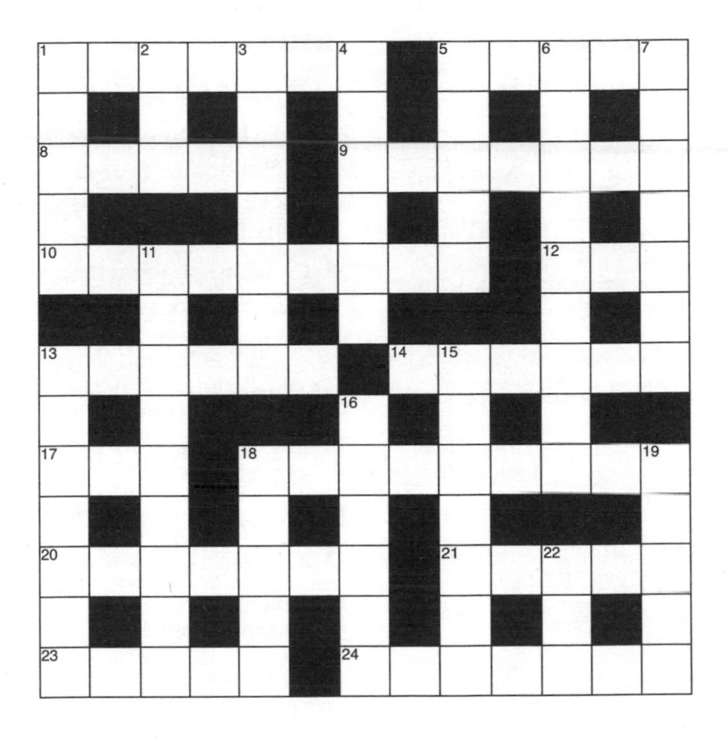
1
2
3
4
5
6
7
8
9
10
11
12
13
14
15
16
17
18
19
20
21
22
23
24

ACROSS

1 Abstemious, sparing (6)

5 Pig flesh (4)

8 Container; sounds like *wan* (4)

9 Unbalanced (3-5)

10 Individual; extraordinary (8)

11 Colleague (4)

12 To slow (development) (6)

14 (Old LP) needle (6)

16 Enormous (4)

18 Touring performance (especially pop) (8)

20 Irish town; type of verse (8)

21 Irregular reading; spot on screen (4)

22 Non-permanent secretary (4)

23 Royal seat (6)

DOWN

2 Bring to fruition (7)

3 Soviet labour camp system (5)

4 Dickens's eponymous Amy (6,6)

5 (Session) of all members (7)

6 Competitor; be as good as (5)

7 Man's (tweed) coat (6,6)

13 Belgian province, Scheldt port (7)

15 Impractically ideal (7)

17 Nimble (5)

19 Dull; sedate; unflamboyant (5)

ACROSS

1 Supporter (6)

4 Of no effect (4)

9 Plant life; Miles's sister (*The Turn of The Screw*) (5)

10 Lowest-form-of-wit practitioner (7)

11 (E.g. bishop) nominal (7)

12 *Prisoner of Chillon* poet (5)

13 Jester's insignia (3,3,5)

17 Photo, stamp book (5)

19 Plotted secretly (7)

22 Spanish red wine/fruit drink (7)

23 Druid priestess (*Bellini opera*) (5)

24 Feel absence of (4)

25 Poach (trout); amuse (6)

DOWN

1 Be appropriate to (5)

2 Zagreb its capital (7)

3 Computer-sent messages (1-4)

5 Say; complete (5)

6 Enticing (6)

7 Love potion (11)

8 Make possible (6)

14 Look up to (6)

15 Inheritance-of-acquired-traits theorist (7)

16 Kidnapper's demand (6)

18 Marriage announcements (5)

20 Vietnam capital (5)

21 Put (cloth) over (5)

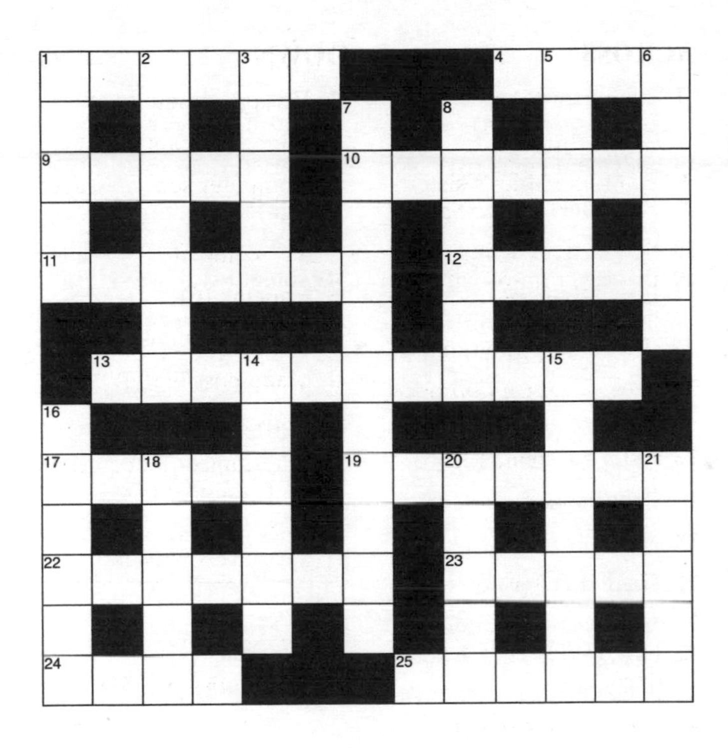

ACROSS

7 US alliance, once v USSR (*abbr.*) (4)

8 Judgment court (8)

9 Regional dialect (6)

10 Servile dependant (6)

11 Lose intensity; (moon) decline from full (4)

12 Missionary efforts (8)

15 Albert –, Nobel physicist (8)

17 Embittered; infertile (land) (4)

18 Shortage (6)

21 Lag behind (6)

22 Husband of Minnehaha (*Longfellow*) (8)

23 A headland; a Loch (4)

DOWN

1 Dancer, World War 1 German spy (4,4)

2 Very serious matter (2,4)

3 Ear-viewing implement (8)

4 Tablet (4)

5 Savoury tart (6)

6 A smoother; his progress, *Hogarth* (4)

13 Baffled by music (4-4)

14 Ungracious (8)

16 Canny (6)

17 Seeding; sounds like *needlework* (6)

19 – Morecambe, comedian (4)

20 Loathe (4)

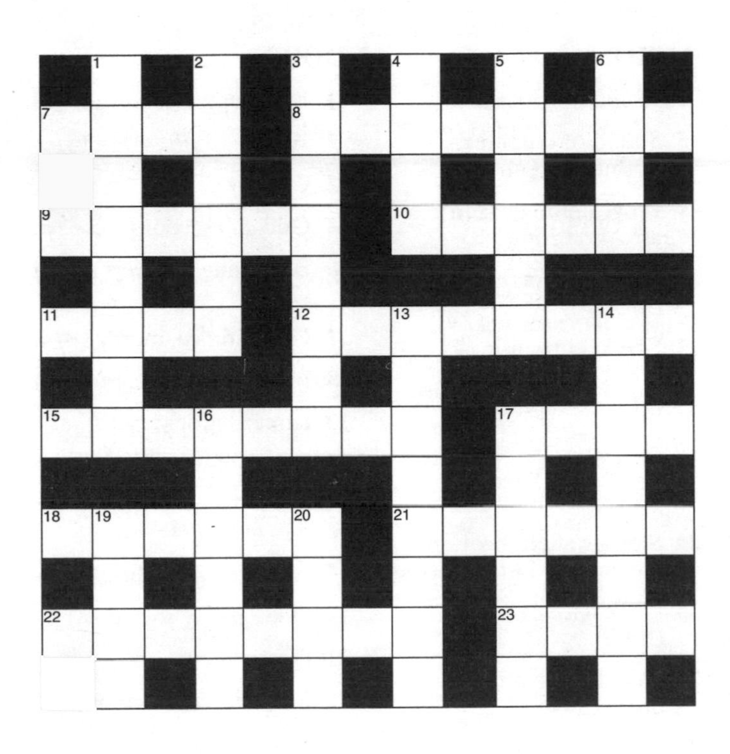

ACROSS

1 Ability to float (8)

5 Sound of laughter, of thunder (4)

9 Programme of character assassination (5,8)

10 Hock; one manipulated (4)

11 Frank; authentic (7)

13 Salad plant; a firework (6)

15 Of milk (6)

18 Wine merchant (7)

20 Storage shelf; broken blown cloud (4)

23 Perfunctory (*ironic*) (5,3,5)

24 Paved enclosure; a distance (4)

25 Missionary keenness (8)

DOWN

1 Bankrupt; a sculpture (4)

2 Work as *Lulu, Aida* (5)

3 Classify (7)

4 Odd coins; reorganise (6)

6 Belonging to a top group (7)

7 Forbearance, mercy (8)

8 Interval of space, time (4)

12 Farcical mockery (8)

14 Points-of-equal-height line (7)

16 Air spray (7)

17 A fruit; a royal house (6)

19 One quickly jotted (4)

21 Deceive (5)

22 Restrain; support; wait (4)

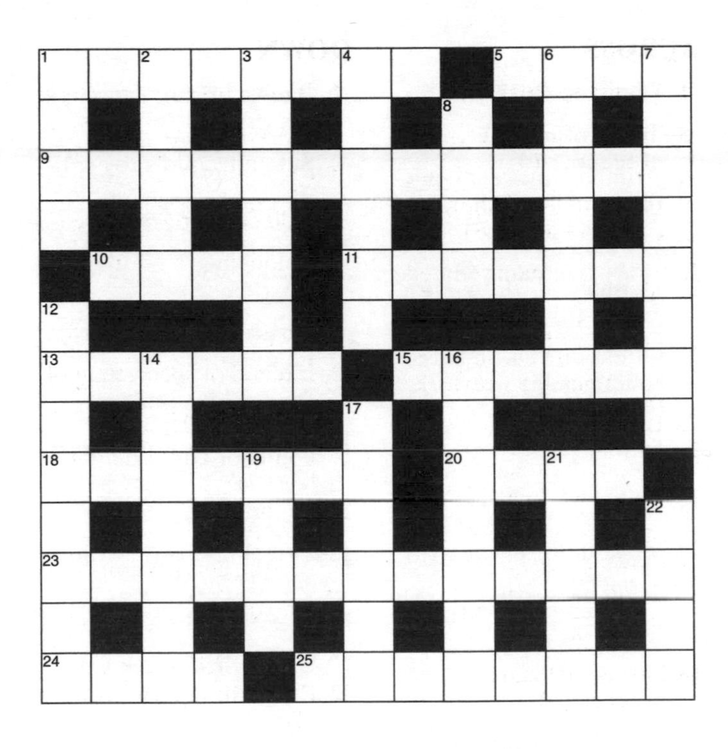

ACROSS

1 Deep puzzle (7)

5 Travel round (4)

8 Irritable; (make it) quick (6)

9 Unrefined (6)

10 Herman —, *Moby-Dick* author (8)

12 Offensive vehicle; large container (4)

13 Bad dream (9)

17 Suspend; execute (4)

18 Exercise rooms (8)

20 Move to lower rank (6)

21 Small beer cask (6)

23 Infant (4)

24 Session (7)

DOWN

2 An American; a multiple bet (6)

3 Summit; child's toy (3)

4 Of the sovereign (5)

5 Italian restaurant (9)

6 Bearlike (6)

7 Howl; something very funny (6)

11 Boastful ostentation (9)

14 Thomas —, *Tom Brown* author (6)

15 Picture taker (6)

16 Immobilise (arms); little cogwheel (6)

19 Civvies; Islamic jurist (5)

22 Deep wheel track (3)

ACROSS

4 Plant's pouch-like cavity (3)

8 Increase, add to (7)

9 (Games, show) ring (5)

10 Ventilated (5)

11 Frame with V-shaped legs (7)

12 Moon-loving shepherd; Keats's subject (8)

14 A service; a quantity (4)

14, 15 Wholesale slaughter (8)

15 1/640th square mile (4)

16 Impurity remover (8)

20 (Special) clothing (7)

21 Disprove; force back (5)

23 Put ball in play; do spell of duty (5)

24 French, Italian Mediterranean coast (7)

25 Add (up); child (3)

DOWN

1 Cope; run (6)

2 Seaweed product (4)

3 Not often (6)

4 Technologically advanced (5-2-3-3)

5 Small role, relief carving (5)

6 Hold back (8)

7 Stands for canvases (6)

13 Laughably inadequate (8)

15 The right to see, get to (6)

17 Reach destination (6)

18 Form of ceremony (6)

19 Peaceful; at low volume (5)

22 Some meat; a complaint (4)

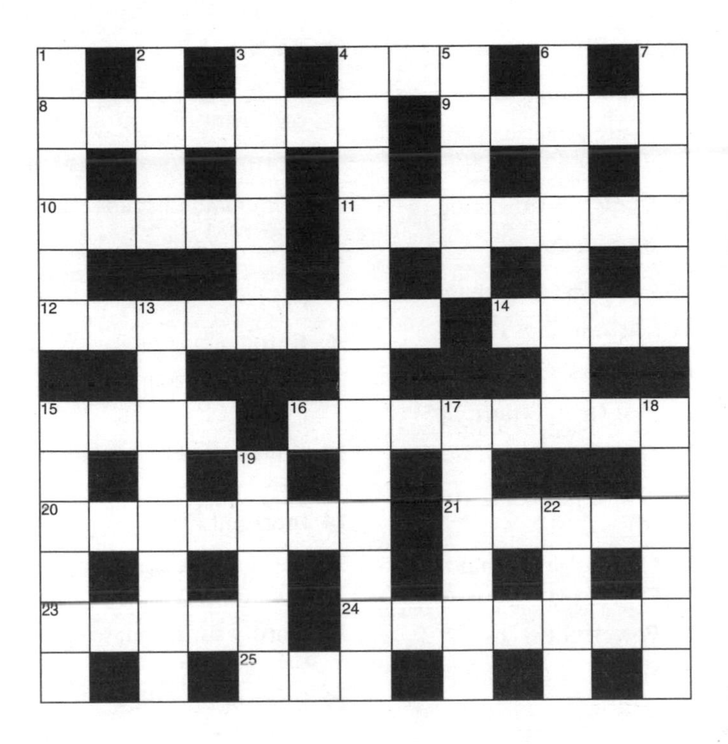

ACROSS

1 Panda food (6)

5 South American animal, its wool (6)

8 Contends (4)

9 More lethal (8)

10 Cut-letter sheet (7)

11 Earth tremor (5)

13 Dickens's David (11)

16 Test (metal) purity (5)

18 Dog-end bowl (7)

21 "Hard pounding" battle (8)

22 Othello's malignant enemy (4)

23 Powerful (6)

24 Imitation (article) (6)

DOWN

2 To do with the largest continent (7)

3 North American ox (5)

4 Commanded; made priest (8)

5 Two Trojan War warriors (4)

6 Befoul (7)

7 Make sure; call at chess (5)

12 (Funds) out of taxman's reach (8)

14 Inert pill (7)

15 Potion; board-game piece (7)

17 Hardly sufficient; to stint (5)

19 Ends of branches; cottons on (5)

20 Advertise; stopper (4)

1
2
3
4
5
6
7
8
9
10
11
12
13
14
15
16
17
18
19
20
21
22
23
24

ACROSS

4 Empty-headed (5)

7 Praiseworthy (8)

8 Run fast; one thrown from oche (4)

9 Latest completion time (8)

10 Impertinent (6)

13 Different people (6)

14 Window-screens; dazzles (6)

15 Teacher; become expert in (6)

18 Making twice as big (8)

19 Offer; elasticity (4)

20 Confirm genuineness of (8)

21 A sense; a sample (5)

DOWN

1 Chemically whiten (6)

2 Busy activity; pad under skirt (6)

3 Virtually not; not at all (6)

4 Feud (8)

5 Gable on e.g. Parthenon (8)

6 Compulsion (6)

11 Refined diners (8)

12 Soft hand-cover; delicate (treatment) (3,5)

14 (Plan within) money limit (6)

15 *One for sorrow* bird (6)

16 Gesture, indication (6)

17 Was jealous of (6)

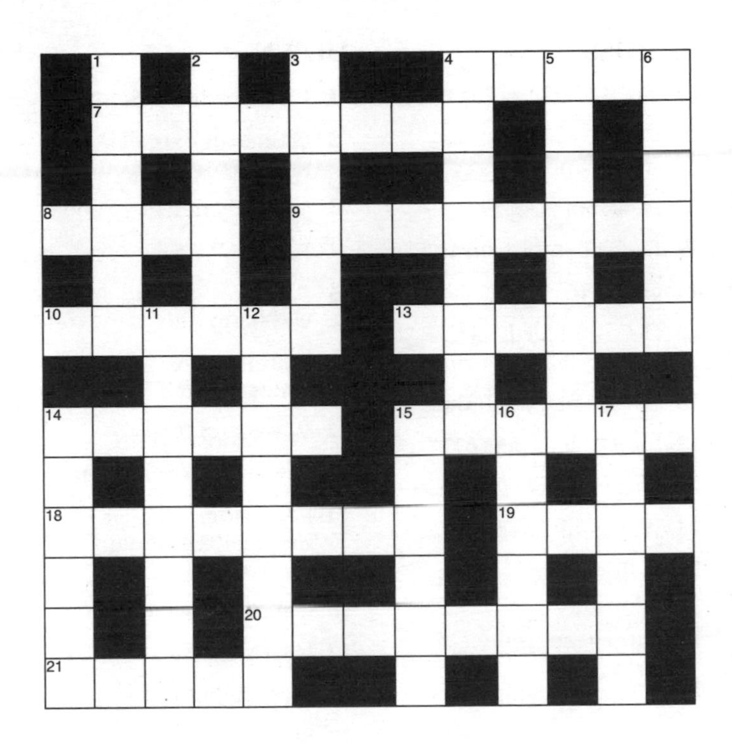
1
2
3
4
5
6
7
8
9
10
11
12
13
14
15
16
17
18
19
20
21

ACROSS

1 *Terrible beauty born* poet (5)

7 (Make) progress (7)

8 A unit of heat (7)

9 Feebleness, infirmity (7)

11 Gullet (6)

13 Cursory, half-hearted (effort) (9)

15 One going on all fours (9)

19 Lion's den man (6)

21 Red bits of US flag (7)

23 Widely liked (7)

24 A flower; *fair, see (anagram)* (7)

25 Large (especially US) farm (5)

DOWN

1 Pleasure craft (5)

2 Glamorous appeal (6)

3 Extend; a risk of middle-age (6)

4 Head of kitchen (4)

5 At mercy of wind and waves (6)

6 Power source; an artillery unit (7)

10 Woken up (6)

12 Right to keep job (6)

14 Food store, (college) shop; tasting of dairy produce (7)

16 Chauffeur; a club (6)

17 Neatly dressed (6)

18 The fiddle (6)

20 Stagger; the abandoned left in it (5)

22 Box; a mineral (4)

ACROSS

1 Race; elan (4)

4 Source of newsprint (4,4)

8 One rung by visitor (8)

9 Greek *I* (4)

10 Ben –, our highest mountain (5)

11 Beethoven opera (7)

13 A slight shaking (6)

15 Secured (good job); having estates (6)

18 Thin, glued board (7)

20 School group; put up (5)

23 – Austen, novelist (4)

24 Green gems (8)

25 Under pressure; accentuated (8)

26 Looked at (4)

DOWN

2 Place of residence (5)

3 Outstanding bravery (7)

4 Work in garden; feeble person (4)

5 Source of "black gold" (8)

6 Value, cost (5)

7 Criss-cross screen (7)

10 Trap; after tax (3)

12 Superior nun (8)

14 Dependent (7)

16 New baby; *no, a teen (anagram)* (7)

17 Female rabbit (3)

19 In what place? (5)

21 Edge furtively along (5)

22 Curve (4)

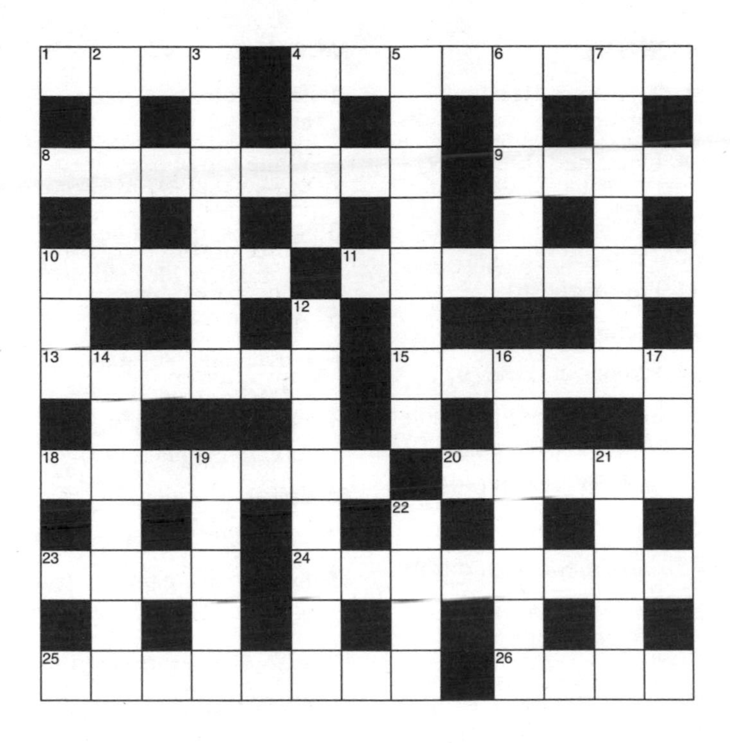

ACROSS

1, 7 Richard III's final defeat (8,5)

8 Unrefined (bread) (9)

9 Total (3)

10 Well off (4)

11 Passionate (6)

13 Lombardy tree (6)

14 Render in stone (6)

17 Seats; hoists in triumph (6)

18 So be it (prayer) (4)

20 Fuss (3)

22 Quasimodo's condition (9)

23 Richard's *kingdom for* it at 1 *ac* (5)

24 Yorkshire town; Henry Tudor earldom (8)

DOWN

1 Shelter; boudoir; an anchor (5)

2 White top of e.g. Mount Fuji (7)

3 Some 5s of the 7 *ac* (4)

4 Speculative idea (6)

5 Wild animal (5)

6 Unyielding (substance) (7)

7 Full competence (in foreign language) (7)

12 Stylish confidence (7)

13 Voracious tropical fish (7)

15 Lower back pain (7)

16 Borneo sultanate (6)

17 Woo; king's retinue (5)

19 Unclothed (5)

21 Iran monarch title once (4)

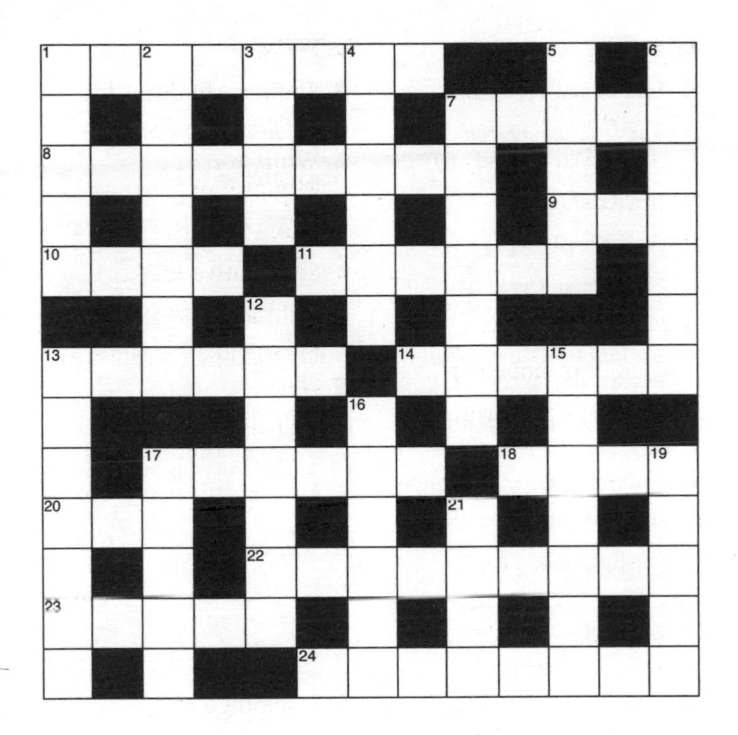

ACROSS

1 File of papers (7)

5 Take water exercise (4)

9 Old gold coin; e.g. Shylock's (5)

10 Aroma; posy (7)

11 Completely mature (bird) (5,7)

12 Thomas –, *Leviathan* author (6)

13 Shock absorber; old fool (6)

16 Where fruitless efforts, storm water, go (4,3,5)

19 Casual, rude (7)

20 Circular painting in relief (5)

21 Sea swell, foam (4)

22 Alpine-plant setting (7)

DOWN

1 Extinct Mauritius bird (4)

2 Give in (to) (7)

3 Egghead (12)

4 Snub (6)

6 Squeezed (5)

7 Bullfighter (7)

8 Involving red tape (12)

12 Very ugly (7)

14 Glazed earthenware (7)

15 Melt down; hand over (6)

17 Thin crisp biscuit (5)

18 Inquisitive (4)

ACROSS

1 Christopher –, discoverer of 6 (8)

5 Go by boat (4)

9 Supernatural (7)

10 Wide expanse of water (5)

11 Univ. athlete; sad (4)

12 A flower; violet antiseptic (7)

14 Lack of interest (6)

16 Pester, hound (6)

19 Curved; mature; pursed (lips) (7)

21 Upper-class person (*derog.*) (4)

24 Birthplace of 1 *ac* (5)

25 Raised-dot writing (7)

26 Endure; final (4)

27 Naively trustful (4-4)

DOWN

1 Army settlement (4)

2 Officially permitted (5)

3 The Scottish play (7)

4 Liquid loss, shortfall (6)

6 The New World (7)

7 Follower of Soviet founder (8)

8 Unite (4)

13 Part-song (8)

15 (Especially US) old boy (7)

17 Insurance statistician (7)

18 Fit to consume (6)

20 Timber; issue cards (4)

22 Female foal (5)

23 Conduct; an element (4)

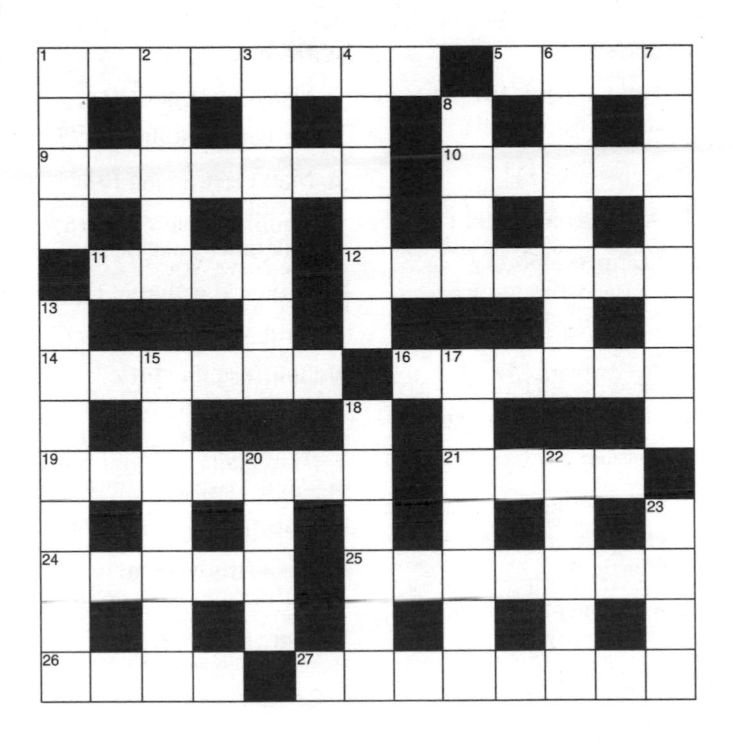

ACROSS

1 Animal panic (8)

5 Profound (4)

8 Rebellion (8)

9 A fish; conical hill (4)

11 Lump; temporary increase (5)

12 Very wicked (7)

13 Apart from (6)

15 Harass; interfere with (6)

18 Passage between seats (7)

19 Orig. name of St Peter (5)

21 (Run) in murderous frenzy (4)

22 More high-pitched (voice) (8)

23 Peel, trim (4)

24 Of the underworld (8)

DOWN

1 Stalks after harvest (7)

2 Of, heard by, the ear (5)

3 Man threatening to queen (6,4)

4 Inflatable boat (6)

6 A typical example (7)

7 Push, importune (5)

10 Ill-affordable little contribution (6,4)

14 Frankness (7)

16 Plant's twining shoot (7)

17 Constricting snake (6)

18 Hold firmly; come to understand (5)

20 Fruit; its *flower gaudy* for Browning (5)

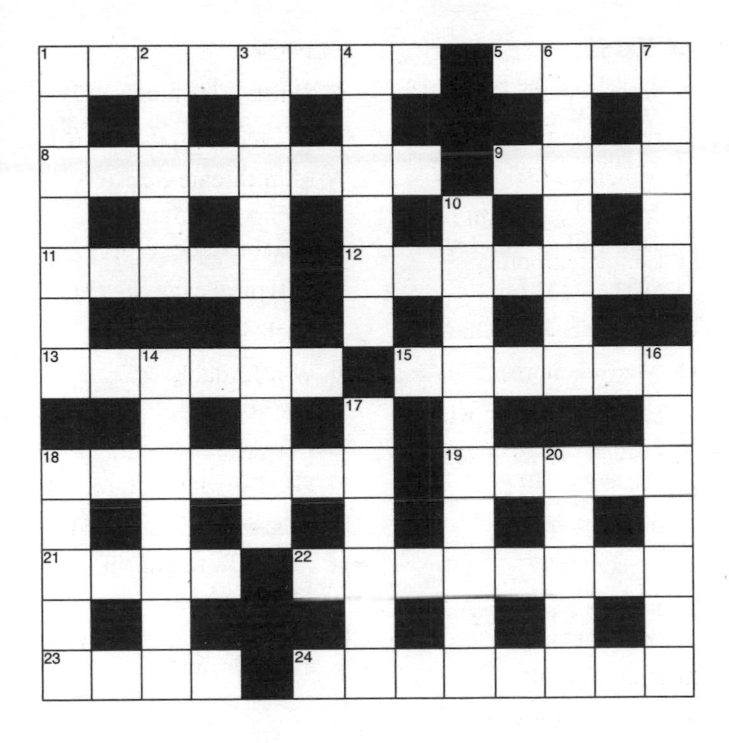
1
2
3
4
5
6
7
8
9
10
11
12
13
14
15
16
17
18
19
20
21
22
23
24

ACROSS

1 One of many born after World War 2 (4,6)

7 A share (7)

8 Condemns (5)

10 Betrayal of country (7)

11 Come up (5)

12 Exhausted, decadent (6)

15 Modern name of Danzig (6)

17 Lampoon (5)

18 Accuse of 10 (7)

21 Sharp point (5)

22 Tiredness (7)

23 Frothy dessert, with marsala (10)

DOWN

1 Warren Hastings opponent; William Hare accomplice (5)

2 Rapture; English composer (5)

3 Fruit, unzip to eat (6)

4 Experienced person (3,4)

5 A wearing away (7)

6 Promotion to divine status (10)

9 Opportunist criminal (5,5)

13 The Sunshine State (7)

14 A thin, lustrous silk fabric (7)

16 Intentional (harm); obstinate (6)

19 Paved terrace (5)

20 Point of view; 5th century invader (5)

ACROSS

1 Definitely; whatever happens (7,4)

7 Hair grip; lose grip (5)

8 Vanity project (3-4)

10 Emotional closeness (8)

11 Part of fish, of mushroom; quarter pint (4)

13 Quick look (6)

15 Drums played on knees (6)

17 Per person (4)

18 Dilemma (8)

21 Be passive; relax (3,4)

22 Name; style (5)

23 Insidious Greek gift (6,5)

DOWN

1 Water source, takes coins (7-4)

2 Curl; Dickens boy (5)

3 Excessively (8)

4 Deep ditch (6)

5 Eden earldom; various rivers (4)

6 Hiding nefariously (7)

9 Rigid, light packaging (11)

12 First rate (3-5)

14 Very old (7)

16 Nepalese soldier (6)

19 Place of sacrifice (5)

20 Ring of light (4)

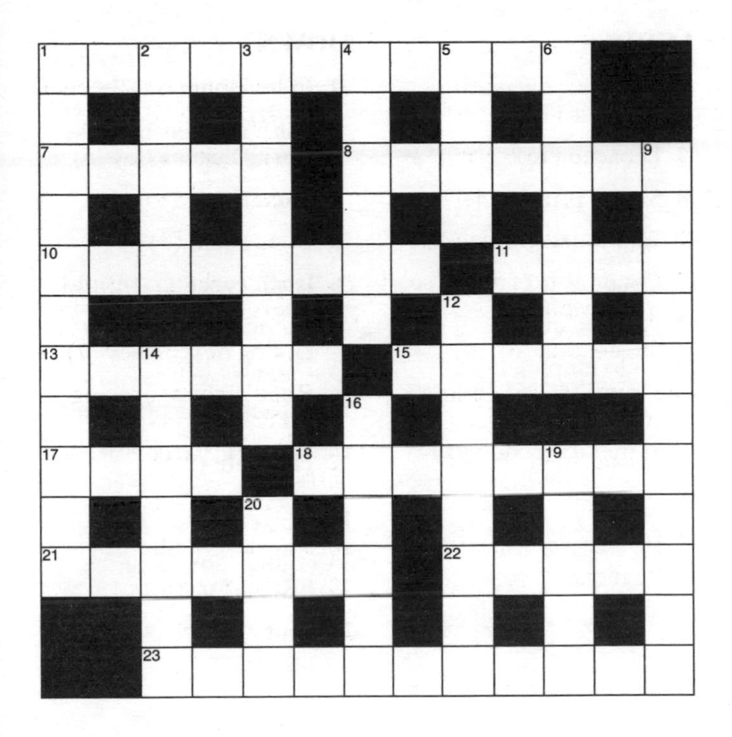

ACROSS

1 Tomorrow; sometime (Spanish) (6)

5 Broached (6)

8 Smart, genteel (4)

9 *Hail Mary* prayer (3,5)

10 Coupons (8)

12 Against; an opponent (4)

13 Fit to employ (6)

15 Penetrate (6)

17 Starch for puddings (4)

19 Renegade (8)

21 Give incentive to (8)

23 Baghdad its capital (4)

24 Invented; composed (quarrel) (4,2)

25 South Devon city (6)

DOWN

2 In loving mood (7)

3 For particular purpose (2,3)

4 Stupefaction (9)

5 Lyric poem (3)

6 Issue, proceed (from) (7)

7 Authoritative order (5)

11 Displace (9)

14 A sedative; a platitude (7)

16 Travesty; party-game act (7)

18 Wafted smell (5)

20 (Clock) sound; agree (with) (5)

22 Unit of current (*abbr.*) (3)

ACROSS

4 Turn up ground (3)

8 Normal course of events (7)

9 Divide in two (5)

10 Elector (5)

11 Bloat (7)

12 Have contrary view (8)

14 Low dam (4)

15 Bird; bit of fun (4)

16 US state; a musical (8)

20 Punish (7)

21 Return to civvy street (5)

23 A female relative (5)

24 Nine-sided figure (7)

25 Dowel; prevent (price) rise (3)

DOWN

1 Shown to be true (6)

2 Smallest piglet (4)

3 E.g. North Sea platform (3-3)

4 Blind navigation (4,9)

5 Phantom (5)

6 Bosom friend (5,3)

7 Supplier of funds (6)

13 Paper ribbon for throwing (8)

15 (Manuscript) gap (6)

17 Giving help (6)

18 Pigment-deficient creature (6)

19 Soak; unfairly expensive (5)

22 Caspar, Melchior, and Balthazar (4)

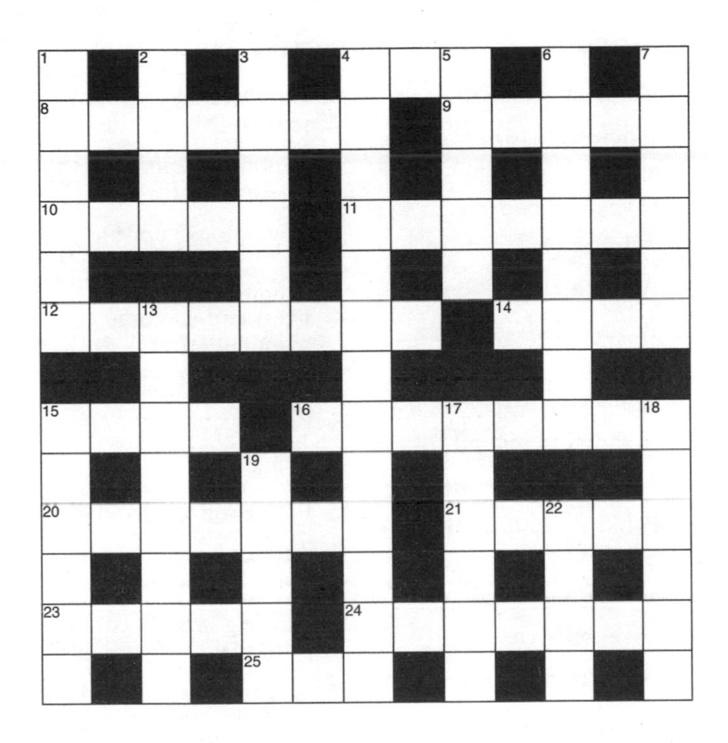
1
2
3
4
5
6
7
8
9
10
11
12
13
14
15
16
17
18
19
20
21
22
23
24
25

ACROSS

1 Company emblem (4)

3 Adolescent (8)

9 Newly made; cold (wind) (5)

10 Allspice (7)

11 A city; a US president (7)

12 Brought into existence (4)

14 China clay (6)

16 A showy perennial (6)

18 Capital of Norway (4)

19 Pablo –, 20th century artist (7)

22 Suitcases; a trollop (7)

23 Give one's view (5)

24 Wind from Continent (8)

25 I've spilled it! (4)

DOWN

1 Resembling the real person (8)

2 Global-warming air pollutant (10,3)

4 Lay out, use up (6)

5 Windhoek its capital (7)

6 President/supreme commander rank (13)

7 A bird; to swindle (4)

8 Go away! (4)

13 Noble lady (8)

15 Post-Bronze period (4,3)

17 Attraction; request to umpire (6)

20 Cut (e.g. wood); cut of pork (4)

21 A reed instrument (4)

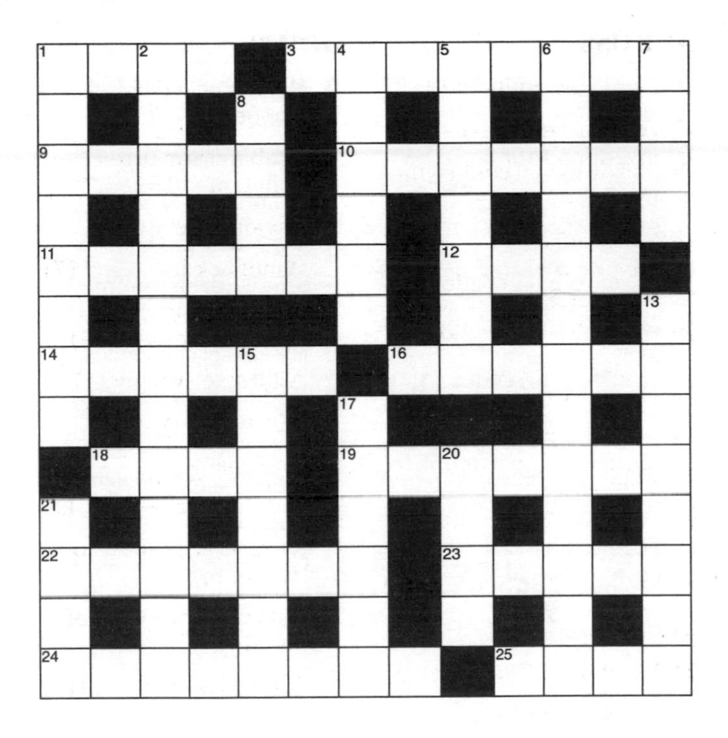

ACROSS

6 Gardening skill (5,7)

7 Obvious; right to exploit invention (6)

8 Flashes of light; ship's radio officer (6)

9 One Zeus visited as swan (4)

10 Billboard; saving (8)

12 Transfer, surrender (4,4)

16 E.g. crocus "bulb" (4)

18 Storage compartment (6)

20 In unfeeling way (6)

21 Feeble, insipid (behaviour) (4-3-5)

DOWN

1 Ely outlaw, opposed Conqueror (8)

2 Grab quickly (6)

3 Spanish carnival (6)

4 Taj Mahal site (4)

5 Smashed; discontinuous (6)

6 Elegance; clemency (5)

11 Reduce by a tenth (8)

13 In fear (6)

14 *Romeo and Juliet* city (6)

15 Fame (6)

17 Governor (5)

19 Ship's track; funeral vigil (4)

1
2
3
4
5
6
7
8
9
10
11
12
13
14
15
16
17
18
19
20
21

ACROSS

1 Start to grow (6)

5 Suit; turn into (6)

8 Jerky shock (4)

9 About to happen (8)

10 Loss of hope (7)

11 Throb, beat (5)

13 Travel widely (3,3,5)

16 European royal house once; some Operas (5)

18 Thoughtful (7)

21 Rudimentary (8)

22 His wife a countess (4)

23 Ski obstacle race (6)

24 Israeli money (6)

DOWN

2 Skill, daring (7)

3 Available whenever wanted (2,3)

4 Gloaming (8)

5 Small protuberance; exclude from plane flight (4)

6 Defeat (7)

7 Take-away (sign) (5)

12 Splinter-removing implement (8)

14 Marking an era (7)

15 Of many different types (7)

17 Make void (5)

19 One from Uppsala (5)

20 Windless (4)

ACROSS

1 Place of activity, danger (3,4)

5 Reeking sunset ran into its Bay (*Browning*) (5)

8 Bird-dung fertiliser (5)

9 Mortification (7)

10 Fruit; Durrell Cyprus book (6,6)

12 Dull-witted; blunt (6)

14 Manage with what one has (4,2)

17 Way of ruinous indulgence (*Shakespeare*) (8,4)

21 Rope; artist (7)

22 Fairy-tale-writing brothers (5)

23 Swagger; strengthening bar (5)

24 Squirting implement (7)

DOWN

1 Intellectual (8)

2 Stretch of ground; pamphlet (5)

3 Declare (e.g. faith) (7)

4 Equipment; get to grips with (6)

5 Amulet; allure (5)

6 Send mad (7)

7 Defined area (4)

11 Geniality (8)

13 Asian primate; *it's rare (anagram)* (7)

15 One getting own back (7)

16 William —, 19th century designer; type of dancer (6)

18 Sacred choral piece (5)

19 Of birds (5)

20 (Musical) work (4)

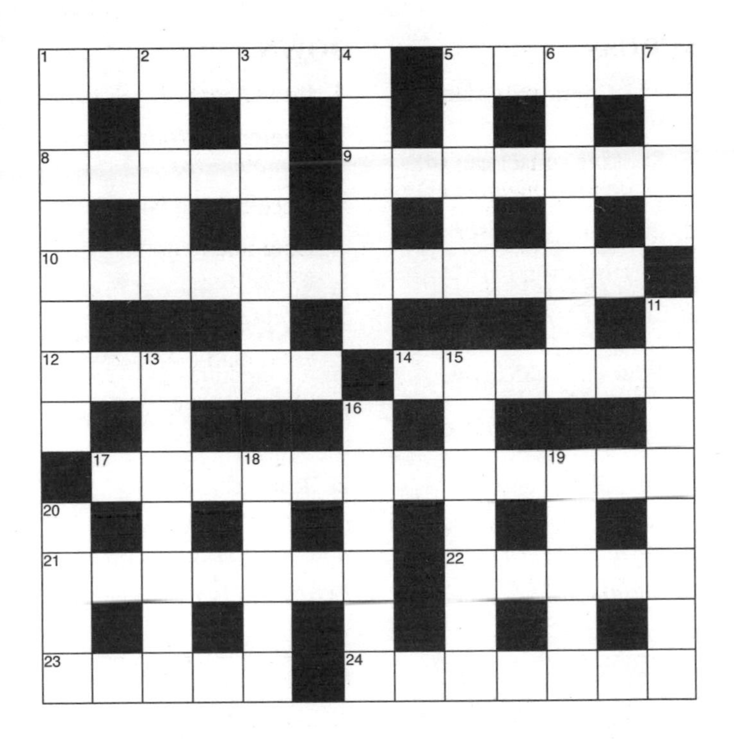
1
2
3
4
5
6
7
8
9
10
11
12
13
14
15
16
17
18
19
20
21
22
23
24

ACROSS

1 The Conqueror's book (8)

5 Speaker's platform (4)

9 Lowers (oneself) (7)

10 Aroma; atmosphere (5)

11 Rely (on) (4)

12 Fighting man (7)

14 John —, *Brief Lives* author (6)

16 Preoccupy (6)

19 One-horn beast (7)

21 Head-covering; US gangster (4)

24 Mindless (5)

25 Pet rodent (7)

26 Unit of heredity (4)

27 Keep safe; a special area (8)

DOWN

1 Lower part of wall (4)

2 Venomous African snake (5)

3 Coruscate (7)

4 Give help (6)

6 Torment oneself (7)

7 Unexpected event (8)

8 Young horse (4)

13 Becoming older, more developed (8)

15 The UK (7)

17 Island group north of Cuba (7)

18 Fix firmly (6)

20 Finished; on top of (4)

22 Target ring furthest from bull (5)

23 At liberty (4)

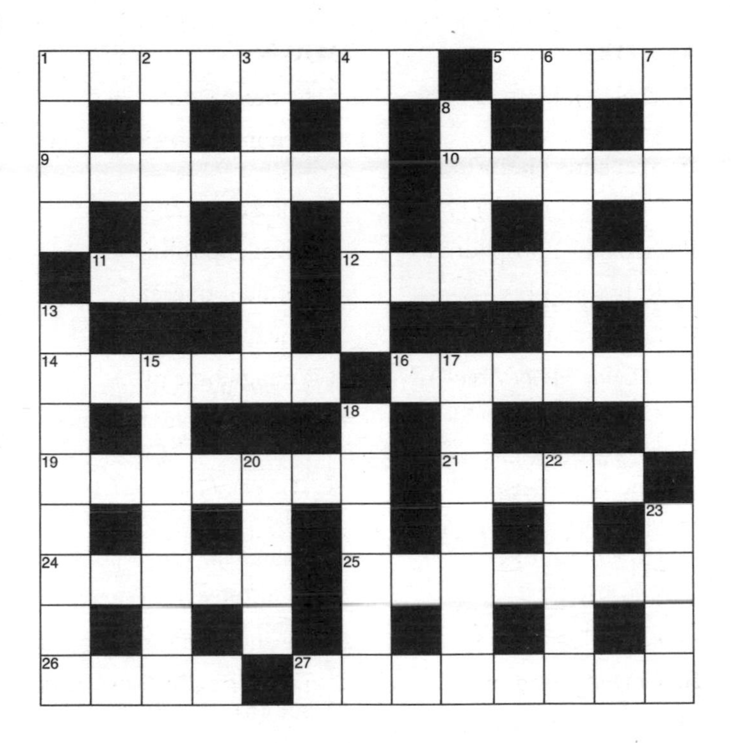

ACROSS

1 *Trout Quintet* composer (8)

5 Predatory animal; eat fast (4)

9 Musical form with repeats (5)

10 Portia's maid (*The Merchant of Venice*) (7)

11 Infringement penalty (7)

12 Container; sink (5)

13 Socially compulsory (2,7)

18 Monastic mountain (5)

20 Bar supporting fanlight (7)

22 Undeviating (imitation) (7)

23 Launcelot –, Shylock's servant (5)

24 Stagger; dance (4)

25 Candour (8)

DOWN

1 Conflict (6)

2 A number; part of county once (7)

3 A fellow (*slang*) (5)

4 Keep good discipline (3,1,5,4)

6 Refuge in trouble (*fig.*) (5)

7 Brandish gloatingly (6)

8 Boy singer (6)

14 Countryman (6)

15 Arousing contempt (7)

16 Thick (ship's) cable (6)

17 Print (characters) in relief (6)

19 Rise and fall (sea) (5)

21 An element; *groan (anagram)* (5)

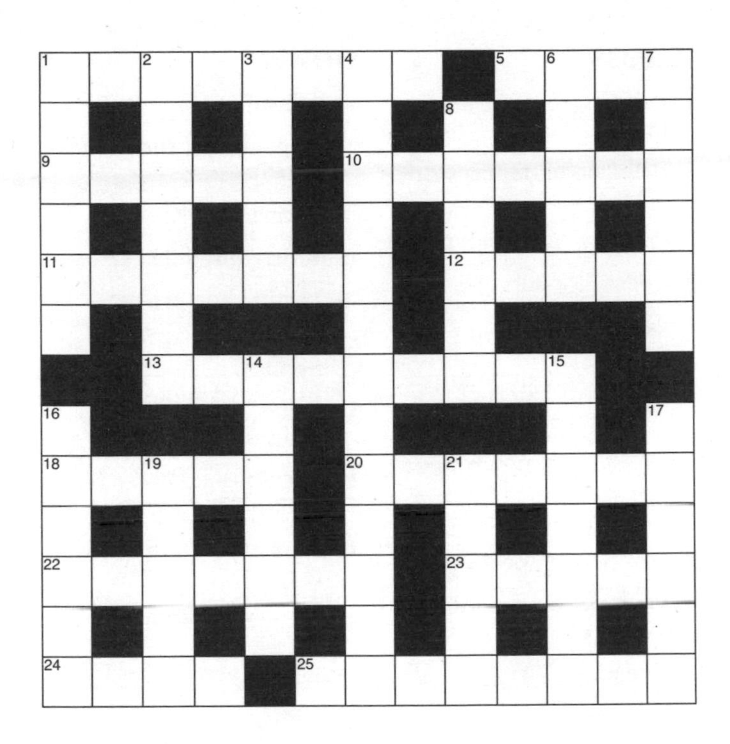
1
2
3
4
5
6
7
8
9
10
11
12
13
14
15
16
17
18
19
20
21
22
23
24
25

ACROSS

1 Pointed (remark, wire) (6)

5 Bring up under pressure (4)

8 Practical joke (4)

9 Logic choppers (8)

10 Canadian east coast district (8)

11 Bunch (of hair) (4)

12 Short-sightedness (6)

14 A tree; smart (6)

16 Hole for e.g. coin (4)

18 One from Papeete (8)

20 Vault rib; base stone of arch (8)

21 Unexciting (4)

22 Fun; taunt (4)

23 Coy, modest (6)

DOWN

2 Out-of-line result (7)

3 Exponent of the *noble art* (5)

4 Drawback (12)

5 Indication, sign (7)

6 Distinctive (artistic) theme (5)

7 Spoils the child? (6,3,3)

13 Defender of one's country (7)

15 Thomas –, *Prayer Book* author (7)

17 Momentary slip; expire (5)

19 Symbolic animal (5)

1
2
3
4
5
6
7
8
9
10
11
12
13
14
15
16
17
18
19
20
21
22
23

ACROSS

2 Voltaire's optimist (*Candide*) (8)

6 Elegant cavalryman (6)

8 Loose collection (6)

9 Australian interior (7)

10 Cloister court; (Northern) yard (5)

12 Ranting speaker (3-7)

16 Fond of company (10)

18 Film for home viewing (5)

20 Rail tracks in yard (7)

21 Wood for furniture; edible wrinkled kernel (6)

22 Vigour (6)

23 Range of freedom (8)

DOWN

1 Heaped, white cloud mass (7)

2 Make (future event) impossible (8)

3 Cause of resentment (6)

4 Regularity; a taxonomic group (5)

5 To foam, be agitated (6)

7 Wrecking activity (8)

11 Guile, subterfuge (8)

13 (New Testament) hypocrite (8)

14 Trunks and cases (7)

15 Affirmation (6)

17 Strongly, healthily built (6)

19 Dutch town, its blue ware (5)

ACROSS

1 Skewered, grilled meat (5)

7 Mediaeval "chemistry" (7)

8 In keen fashion (7)

9 Slovenly dirtiness (7)

11 Deplore (6)

13 Only country to leave European Community (9)

15 One taken for ride (9)

19 Imitated (6)

21 Crowded, nestled together (7)

23 Pleasant, available service (7)

24 Range of hearing (7)

25 One from another planet (5)

DOWN

1 Tolling of bell (5)

2 Having too many wives (6)

3 A strait; sounds like *orientation* (6)

4 Paths; methods (4)

5 Servitude (6)

6 Seize and detain (7)

10 Canada's largest province (6)

12 Hypnotised state (6)

14 Japanese warrior (7)

16 Deliberate cruelty (6)

17 Ivanhoe's girl (*Sir Walter Scott*) (6)

18 Skimpy beachwear (6)

20 Senior member (5)

22 Items of information (4)

ACROSS

1 Come to bad conclusion (3,2,5)

8 Unacceptably different (7)

9 Dried coconut (5)

10 Fish; part of shoe (4)

11 Feeling sick; offensive (8)

13 Horse-rider (6)

15 Ornamental cave (6)

17 Blend, merge (8)

18 Studious pupil (4)

21 Rye-afflicting fungus (5)

22 In a perfect world (7)

23 Salvation; conversion into cash (10)

DOWN

2 Part of body; type of orange (5)

3 Mosque prayer leader (4)

4 Venetian painter, his auburn shade (6)

5 Pedigree (8)

6 Uphold, sustain (7)

7 *Forsyte* creator (10)

8 Book cover (4,6)

12 Down in dumps (8)

14 Bad error, especially when dropped (7)

16 (Church) division (6)

19 I shall obey (*radio*) (5)

20 Written material for study (4)

ACROSS

1 Cuts; journalists (5)
4 Temporarily inactive (7)
8 Lovingly bring up (7)
9 Area of expertise (5)
10 Table covering (5)
11 Such a Fleece, a Horde, a Gate Bridge (6)
13 Former Spanish dictator (6)
15 Pressure line on weather map (6)
18 A symbiotic plant (6)
20 Europe/US golf cup (5)
22 A horned beast (5)
23 Make aware (7)
24 Shyness (7)
25 Boat Race team (5)

DOWN

1 Secure (wrists) (8)
2 Argentina city; Moorish Spain capital (7)
3 Melting snow (5)
4 A seabed scoop (6)
5 Charity events; a gentleman burglar (7)
6 Sharp mountain ridge (5)
7 Fuss (2-2)
12 Salacious (8)
14 (In) league (7)
16 Starting to sprout (7)
17 Ill repute (6)
19 Covered in creeper (5)
20 Money in India (5)
21 (Glass) be very full (4)

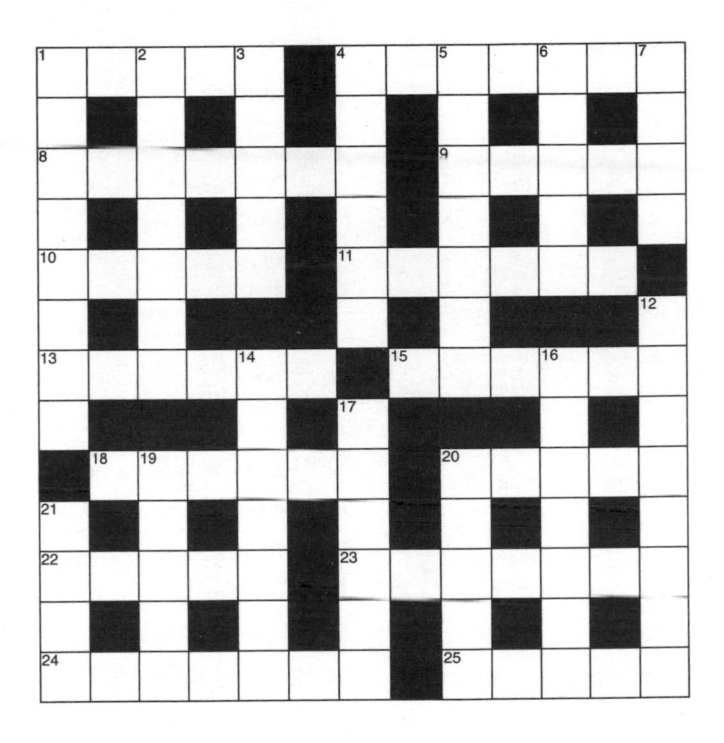

ACROSS

1 In which Po rises (4)

3 Surrey town, sounds like *marks* (7)

8 Busily active (2,3,2)

9 Samuel –, electric telegraph inventor (5)

10 Run away to marry (5)

11 Disappoint; lowered (3,4)

13 General agreement (9)

17 Make anxious (7)

19 Muslim saviour (5)

20 Tedium (5)

22 Attack (7)

23 Outrageous, corrupting (7)

24 Group of girls, of quail (4)

DOWN

1 Loved (6)

2 Policing vehicle (6,3)

3 The scapula (8,5)

4 Let in; confess (5)

5 And not (3)

6 18th century author; sounds like *severe* (6)

7 *Thick* on it *snow the leaves (Wenlock Edge)* (6)

12 Hop-kiln building (4,5)

14 Spicy fried pastry (6)

15 Mph indicator (*abbr.*) (6)

16 Very unclean (6)

18 Join in one (5)

21 Numbers (*abbr.*) (3)

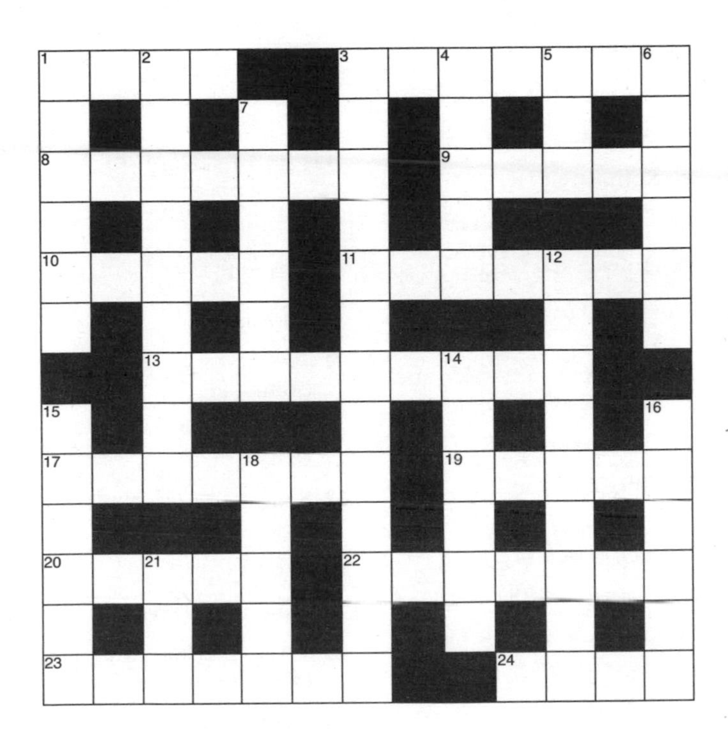
1
2
3
4
5
6
7
8
9
10
11
12
13
14
15
16
17
18
19
20
21
22
23
24

ACROSS

1 Nosegay (4)

3 Widely scattered (3-5)

8 Suffocate (7)

10 –jar; –life; –shade (5)

11 A deserved fall (4-7)

13 Delivery chit; certificate (6)

15 Wooster's battleaxe aunt (*Wodehouse*) (6)

17 Go separate ways (4,7)

20 Heraldic blue (5)

21 Keats *half in love with* such *Death* (7)

22 Evanescent (8)

23 Some ice; sounds like *move as liquid* (4)

DOWN

1 Essential part of address (8)

2 Force-ten wind (5)

4 Curt; steep (6)

5 Frivolous goings-on (3,3,5)

6 Ointment (7)

7 French rural holiday home (4)

9 Confinement to home (5,6)

12 Senior Service shade (4,4)

14 Seize (7)

16 Hide from view (6)

18 Terrifying; bad (*loosely*) (5)

19 Neglected child (4)

ACROSS

1 Boring, unvarying voice (8)

5 Wife of Zeus (4)

9 Cardinals collectively (6,7)

10 Had sensation (of); a material (4)

11 Brought into effect; asked (for) (7)

13 Horse gait; won easily, at this (6)

15 (Customs) permit (6)

18 That can be defended (7)

20 Small restaurant (4)

23 Phone-wire support (9,4)

24 Criminal's blunt weapon ... (4)

25 ... his sharp one (8)

DOWN

1 Deer secretion; type of rose (4)

2 Mother-of-pearl (5)

3 Playhouse (7)

4 What bees collect (6)

6 Dry summer Mediterranean wind (7)

7 Humorous story (8)

8 Collapse; disaster (4)

12 Transported with joy (8)

14 Perplex (7)

16 Intoxicant (7)

17 Withdraw (opinion) (6)

19 Insects; a cartoon Bunny (4)

21 Money in till; carnival vehicle (5)

22 Short note (4)

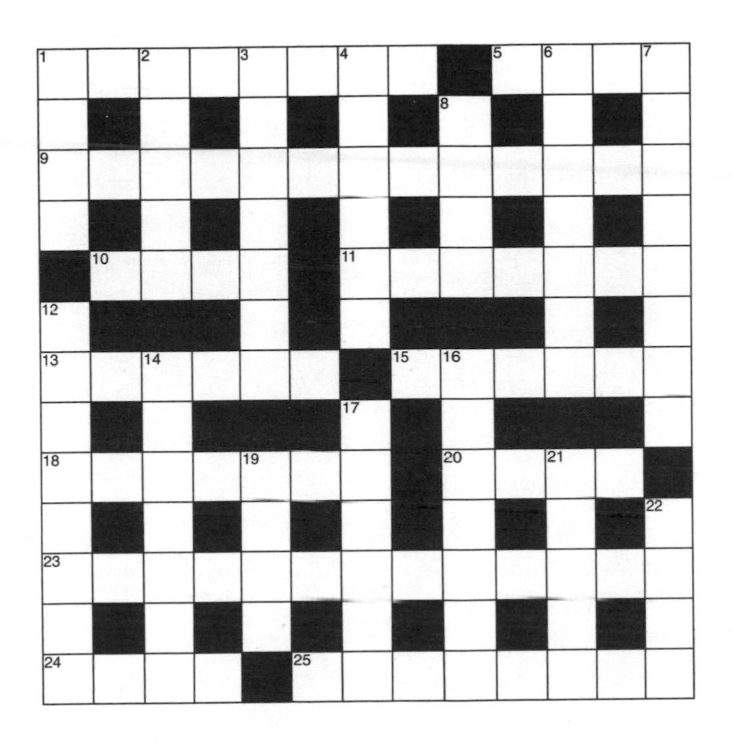

ACROSS

1 Cloak with pretence (9)

6 Dandy (3)

8 Travel over; lie on and hide (5)

9 Researcher (7)

10 Squat down (6)

12 Type of wheat; signified (5)

13 Franklin — Roosevelt (6)

14 Cartoon hero; servant (6)

17 A sense; a vision (5)

19 Affront (6)

21 Sir Winston L. — Churchill (7)

22 A snap (5)

23 Fail; one irrevocably cast (3)

24 Issued (drugs) (9)

DOWN

1 Cut; a remedial leaf (4)

2 Some, not many (7)

3 Part of body, of cereal (3)

4 Percy — Shelley (6)

5 New Testament book; Diana worshippers (9)

6 Untrue (5)

7 Stern, plain-living moralist (7)

11 Having escaped detection (9)

13 Obsolete (7)

15 Richard — Nixon (7)

16 Tree as lemon, lime (6)

18 Parson's land once (5)

20 Alfred, — Tennyson (4)

22 Food with crust (3)

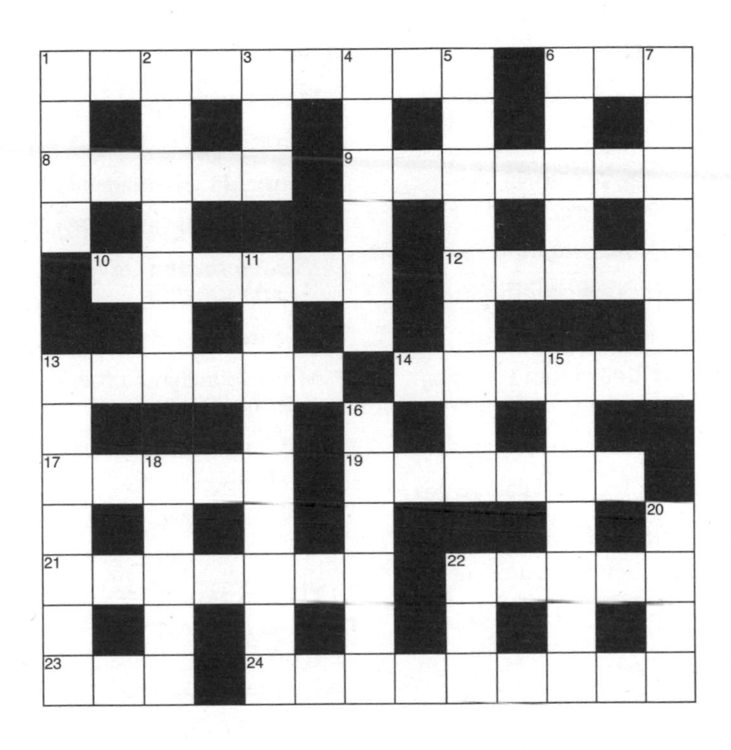

ACROSS

1 Early Dickens work (8,2,3)

8 Protective cover (7)

9 Prison; neglected state (5)

10 Dismissed; flowering (3)

11 Sticking condition (8)

13 Exculpatory reason (6)

14 (Clothes) not covering enough (6)

17 Splendid (8)

19 Professional charge (3)

21 Egyptian dam (5)

22 Infective organism (7)

24 Stealthy (13)

DOWN

1 Surgeon (*derog.*) (8)

2 Flexible (7)

3 National team place (3)

4 Uninhibitedly crude (6)

5 Vicious villain (*Oliver Twist*) (4,5)

6 Brainless beauty (5)

7 Move fast; change focus quickly (4)

11 Self-confidence; pledge of support (9)

12 Mountains Andorra lies in (8)

15 Sicilian gangster (7)

16 Hand over; carry out (crime) (6)

18 Further down (5)

20 Luggage; I claim! (4)

23 An animal; a boat (*abbr.*) (3)

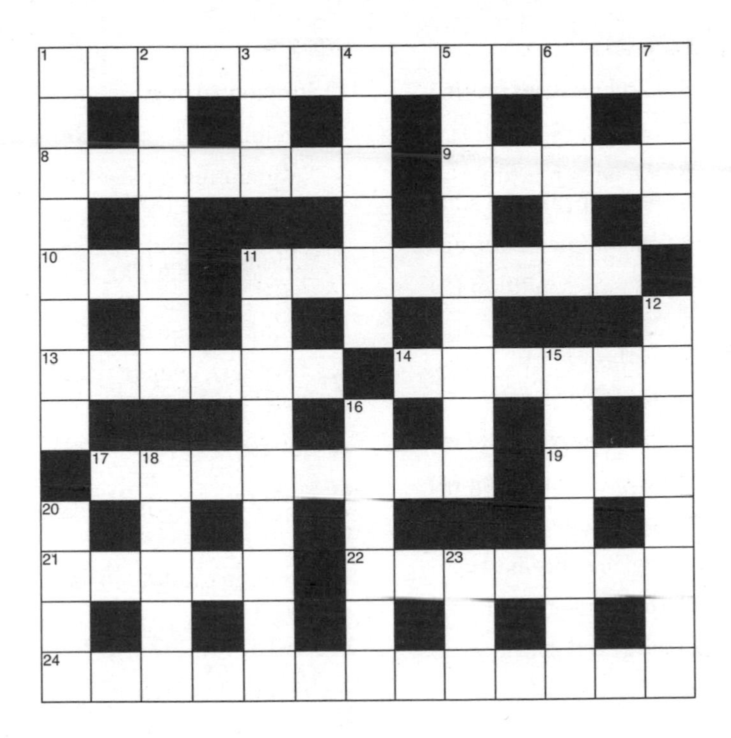
1
2
3
4
5
6
7
8
9
10
11
12
13
14
15
16
17
18
19
20
21
22
23
24

ACROSS

1 Cloth; a structure (6)

5 University grounds (6)

8 Weaving machine; be near (4)

9 One implementing will (8)

10 Hilltop fire (6)

12 Sort, class (4)

15 Terrified (5-8)

16 Advantage; rim (4)

17 Items for meeting (6)

19 Confident; categorical (8)

21 Decline; basin (4)

22 Projecting rim (6)

23 Powerful shock, wound (6)

DOWN

2 Previously mentioned (9)

3 An animal; force down (3)

4 Least soiled (8)

5 Corner of sail; hammock thread; sounds like *hint* (4)

6 Face hair (9)

7 Strange celestial sight (*abbr.*) (3)

11 Yardstick (9)

13 Nom de plume (9)

14 Most general (8)

18 Heap; foundation beam (4)

20 Bird; loved Pussy-cat (*Lear*) (3)

21 – Fever (*Masefield*) (3)

ACROSS

7 Non-clergy (5)

8 Visualise (7)

9 Enormous (7)

10 Tiniest amount (5)

11 Manifest (4)

12 Very bad (8)

15 Frozen sweet (3,5)

16 Slight problem (4)

19 England/Australia cricket trophy (5)

21 Set up ready for use (7)

22 Mutually decide about (5,2)

23 Release (knot) (5)

DOWN

1 Tongues of fire (6)

2 Cutting-edge sharpener (8)

3 Eagles' nest (5)

4 Posed scene (7)

5 Egypt princess, dies with Rhadames (4)

6 Legume seed, in soups etc. (6)

8 Drunkenness (11)

13 Painting, sculpture, etc. (4,4)

14 Flourish (7)

15 *Comfort ye, my people* prophet (6)

17 Ship's kitchen (6)

18 Number of magazine (5)

20 Animal, mad in spring (4)

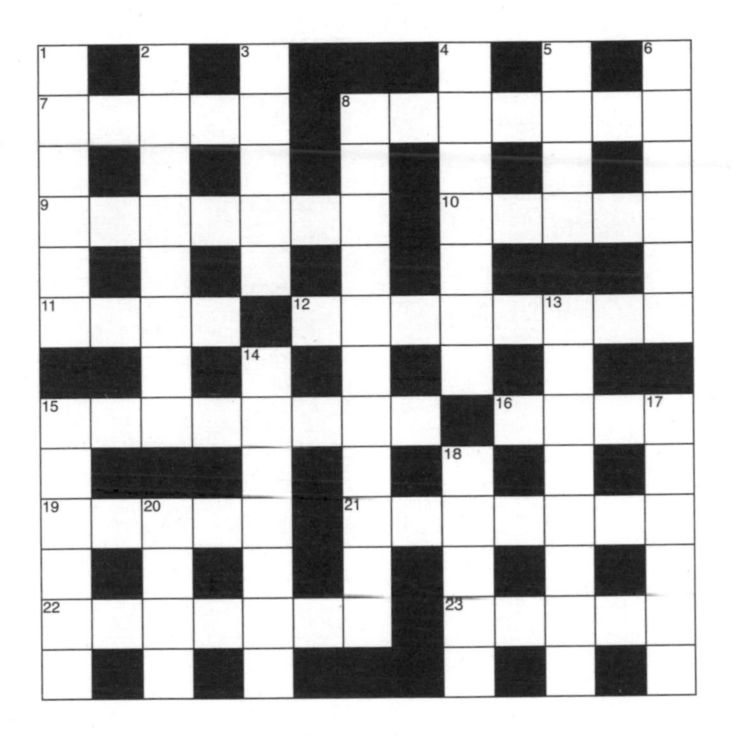

ACROSS

5 One taken with incredible claim (1,5,2,4)

8 Sugared almond; cake-decoration ball (6)

9 Harass (6)

10 Actual event (4)

12 He's from Barcelona (7)

14 Wither (7)

15 Inter-family quarrel (4)

17 Handsome (Greek) youth (6)

18 One awkward at sea (6)

20 Dangerous person (4,8)

DOWN

1 Hangover-curing drink (4,2,3,3)

2 Call up; circle (4)

3 Hide (7)

4 Judge roughly (8)

6 Masticate (4)

7 Keep making new discoveries (4,3,5)

11 Smoke vents (8)

13 Temperature scale (7)

16 Boring; place to live (4)

19 Explosive weapon (4)

ACROSS

1 Naughty child; pile-driving hammer (6)

4 Teasing problem (6)

8 Punted canal boat (7)

10 Routine; boring instrument (5)

11 Single entity (4)

12 Equity (8)

14 Very tasty (9)

18 Diligence; manufacturing (8)

20 Impossible, forbidden (2-2)

22 Hebridean island, south of Uists (5)

23 Senior naval officer (7)

24 Erred; showed assent (6)

25 Headlong course (6)

DOWN

1 Double-size champagne bottle (6)

2 Over-fussily protected (7)

3 Cupid (4)

5 Less-fancied competitor (8)

6 Kinshasa its capital (5)

7 Join up (6)

9 The monkey puzzle tree (9)

13 Controlled slide; a ballet step (8)

15 Whip; one harassing (7)

16 *Decline and Fall* historian (6)

17 Egregious error (6)

19 Took a risk (5)

21 Jane Austen's Miss Woodhouse (4)

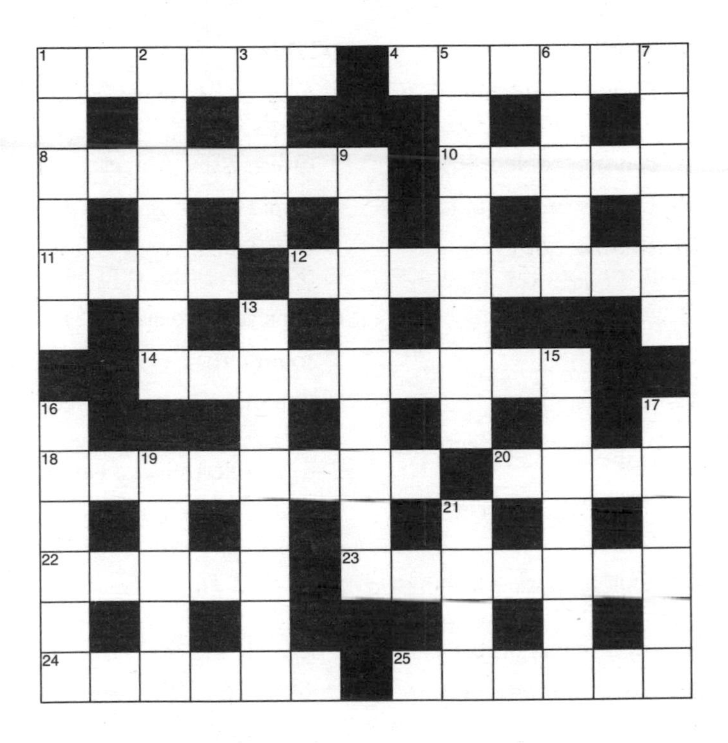

ACROSS

1 Slickly plausible (4)

4 US train system; unfairly compel (8)

8 Defensive gate-tower (8)

9 Reliable bet (4)

10 Queen – Antoinette (5)

11 Took lead role (in) (7)

13 Hold out enticingly (6)

15 Forward stampede (6)

18 Half-man half-horse (7)

20 Seize without right (5)

23 Daybreak (4)

24 Unable to meet debts (8)

25 Lifting power; influence (8)

26 Small (skirt, car) (4)

DOWN

2 Capital of Tibet (5)

3 Going up and down with waves (7)

4 Hard material; type of music (4)

5 Engine starter (8)

6 Competitive runner (5)

7 Stuffy, close (7)

10 Dirt; one's name, if unpopular (3)

12 Half-shadow area (8)

14 Mean, normal (7)

16 Dais (7)

17 A fruit; a joint (3)

19 Hint of colour (5)

21 North Yorkshire cathedral city (5)

22 Leg joint (4)

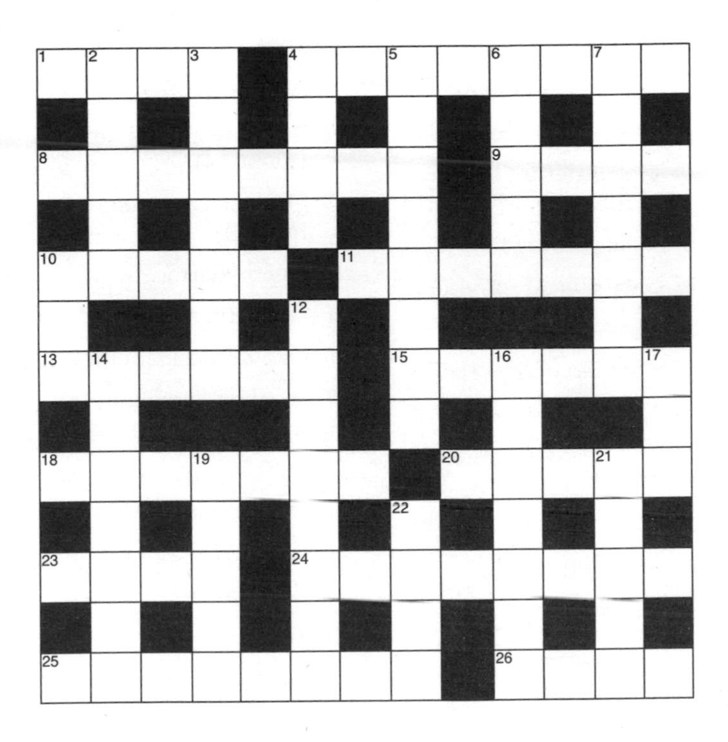

ACROSS

8 Not taking sides (7)

9 Stage (in process) (5)

10 One different from rest (3,3,3)

11 Hole-making tool (3)

12 Shed coat (5)

14 Nervousness (7)

15 *Podsnap, Heep* creator (7)

17 Breathes rapidly (5)

19 Part of fish; a deer (3)

20 Lasciviously excite (9)

22 Set of links (5)

23 Answer (7)

DOWN

1 Advise, tell (6)

2 Tobacco lump; pound (*slang*) (4)

3 Ostentatious remorse (6-7)

4 Not quite (6)

5 (Military) neatness (4,3,6)

6 One from Honolulu (8)

7 A raptor; a magician (6)

13 Personification of US (5,3)

15 Order; straight (6)

16 (Surgical) seam (6)

18 Regular (6)

21 Tiniest amount (*fig.*) (4)

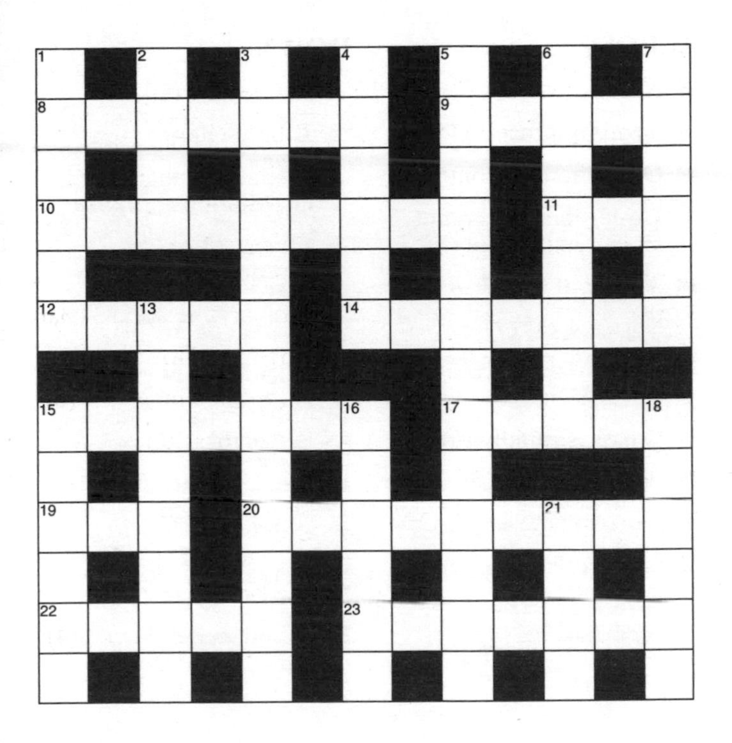

ACROSS

1 Absolute hush (7)

5 Enormous (4)

8 Officer's side-arm (6)

9 Unsubstantiated report (6)

10 Author of *Emma Bovary* (8)

12 Guessing game (1-3)

13 Rules of behaviour (9)

17 A tree; part of hand (4)

18 An idealised rustic (8)

20 Too old, feeble (4,2)

21 Intermittent-motion transmitter (6)

23 Seed; bacillus (4)

24 Not deep (7)

DOWN

2 Frozen drip (6)

3 A newt (3)

4 Produce young; sounds like *slice meat* (5)

5 Clumsy (3-6)

6 Surly (6)

7 Twist in agony (6)

11 Final demand (9)

14 Mineral, its crystal in clocks (6)

15 Little savoury bite (6)

16 Summer-house (6)

19 Apprehend; trick; one worth marrying (5)

22 Friend, mate (3)

ACROSS

1 Male animal; one passed, to avoid blame (4)

3 Omnipresence (8)

8 Ancient Egypt monument (7)

10 Become liable for (5)

11 Madeleines; *so peck, Agnes (anagram)* (6,5)

13 Magic remedy (6)

15 Start (fire) (6)

17 Zest for living (4,2,5)

20 Gorse (5)

21 Decorate (food) (7)

22 Actor's, singer's test (8)

23 Stitched (4)

DOWN

1 Avoided, driven round (2-6)

2 Interesting, rare, item (5)

4 Upper part of dress (6)

5 Mercury (11)

6 Cut, scored (into) (7)

7 Tale; thread (4)

9 Splendid (11)

12 Charity-funding TV evening (8)

14 Wounded (7)

16 Slow (*music*) (6)

18 Opinion; ability to speak (5)

19 Dyke-building Mercian (4)

ACROSS

1 Large animals hunted (3,4)

5 Prime Minister once; flake off (4)

9 Pastoral lover (5)

10 Nauseously sweet (7)

11 Fired with keenness (12)

12 Roof of mouth (6)

13 A sly one; Toad Hall invader (*Grahame*) (6)

16 Transparently honest (7,5)

19 Gulf island sheikdom (7)

20 Write in capitals (5)

21 Religious teacher; expert (4)

22 Where King John lost crown jewels (3,4)

DOWN

1 Soak up sun, praise (4)

2 Hooked grabber; little anchor (7)

3 Shakespeare's wife (4,8)

4 Surfeit (6)

6 Have life (5)

7 Rational (7)

8 When (e.g. sun) disc vanishes (5,7)

12 (Lots of) incoming mail (7)

14 Power of endurance (7)

15 Baby swan (6)

17 Attendant (5)

18 Mormon state (4)

ACROSS

1 Big (plane, crossword) (5)

4 Live together (7)

8 Emily Brontë's *Heights* (9)

9 Flightless bird; a federal project (*abbr.*) (3)

10 Connecting piece (4)

11 Ran fast, naked (8)

13 Dull, boring (6)

14 Fuelling tanker (6)

17 Last round in knock-out (3,5)

19 Prima donna (4)

22 Spoil (3)

23 Robin Hood's jolly monk (5,4)

24 Devotion (7)

25 Wilkie Collins's *Woman in* it (5)

DOWN

1 Precious stone (5)

2 Type of performance, jacket, idol (7)

3 Cooker (4)

4 A patterned cotton (6)

5 A French Protestant (8)

6 Dickens's *House* (5)

7 Stormy peal (7)

12 Prolific; profitable (8)

13 In units of ten (7)

15 Spurs to action (7)

16 Thackeray's *Fair* (6)

18 A social; person (in lawsuit) (5)

20 Low leg joint (5)

21 Front of vessel (4)

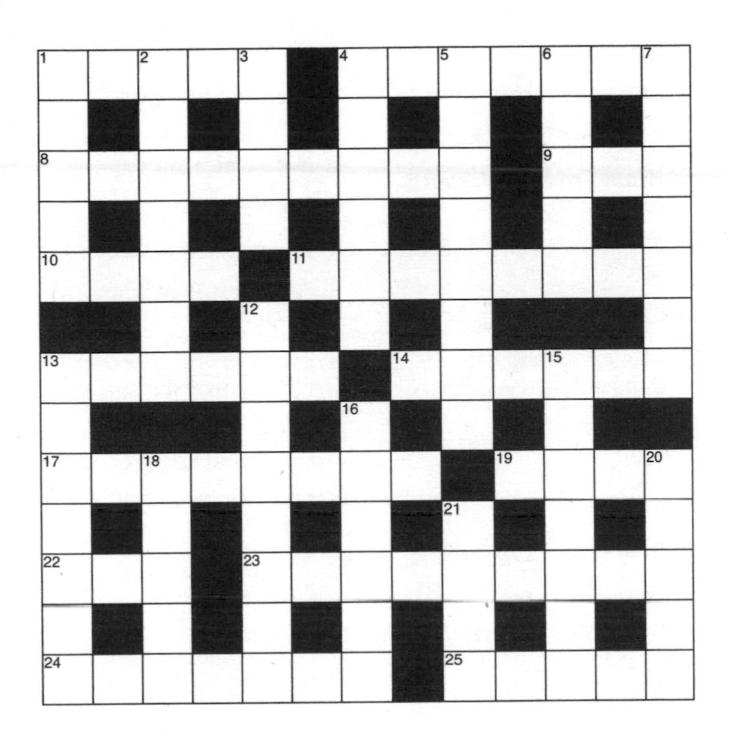

ACROSS

7 The blackthorn (4)

8 Persuasively spoken (8)

9 Boring person (*slang*); his coat (6)

10 Those accepting (e.g. bet) (6)

11 Churl (4)

12 Money earned on deposit (8)

15 Foreword (8)

17 Mountain-top (4)

18 Swift; punctual (6)

21 Beat (cornstalks) (6)

22 Dark (night) (8)

23 Charity bazaar (4)

DOWN

1 Commotion; loud resonance (8)

2 Native servant (6)

3 Feeble person (8)

4 Defensive water (4)

5 Follower of William Penn (6)

6 Trunk protuberance; grade (*reversed*) (4)

13 Formal academic work (8)

14 Sporadic, scattered state (8)

16 Thin plate (e.g. of mineral) (6)

17 To filter, cleanse (6)

19 Civil commotion (4)

20 Level, row (4)

ACROSS

1 Confirm (6)

7 Cloud over, dim (6)

8 Impose control over (8)

10 Neck of land (7)

11 Sort of small peach (7)

12 South American range (5)

14 Scandinavian cave-dweller (5)

15 Unpleasant (5)

19 Diplomatic (7)

20 Exact copy (7)

22 (For) all time (8)

23 Behind (ship) (6)

24 One with blue pencil (6)

DOWN

1 In words (6)

2 Strict, unbending (8)

3 Great happiness (8)

4 Fifteenth (of Roman March) (4)

5 Ragged child (6)

6 Disprove (6)

9 Retributive action (3,3,3)

12 (Eating) not the set meal (1,2,5)

13 Scottish town; *firm sued (anagram)* (8)

16 Opposed (to) (6)

17 Steering handle (6)

18 Competitor in game (6)

21 Small coin; sounds like *given errand* (4)

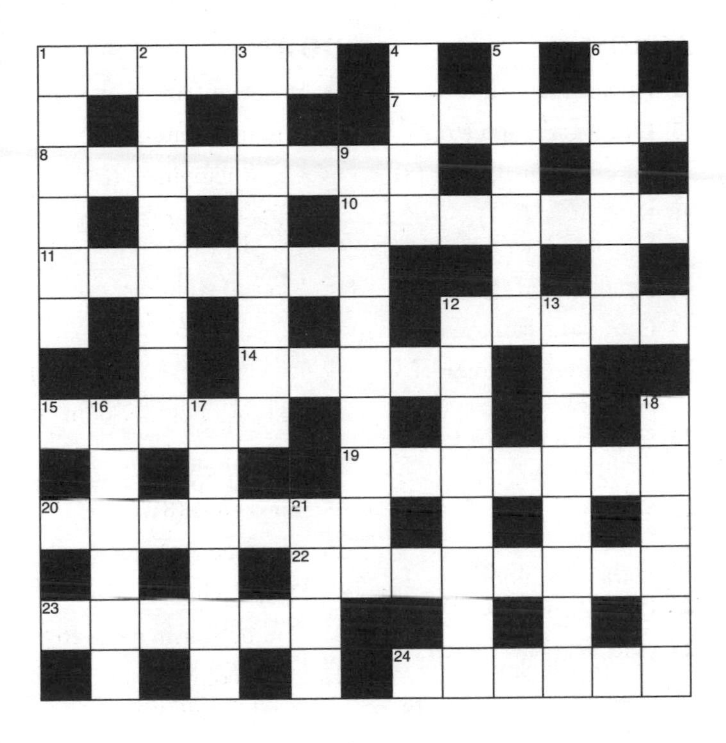

ACROSS

1 Painstaking (9)

6 Deep hole; part of theatre (3)

8 Reprove (7)

9 Slim and long-limbed (5)

10 Bend; cable (4)

11 Grotesque carving (8)

13 Venice business centre once (6)

14 Steppes; a US Presidential birthplace (6)

17 Sir John —, was Poet Laureate (8)

18 Mark of wound (4)

20 Nag; colic (5)

21 Mound-building insect (7)

22 Record; one put on fire (3)

23 Glare of publicity (9)

DOWN

1 Water-holding rock (7)

2 Making threatening gestures (5-8)

3 Double; sounds like *combat* (4)

4 Passé (3-3)

5 Conflict (8)

6 Parsimonious (5-8)

7 Oberon knew a bank where it blew (5)

12 Exquisitely delicate (8)

15 Snake; a deceiver (7)

16 A cock; a fighting weight (6)

17 Jewish roll (5)

19 Paperless exam (4)

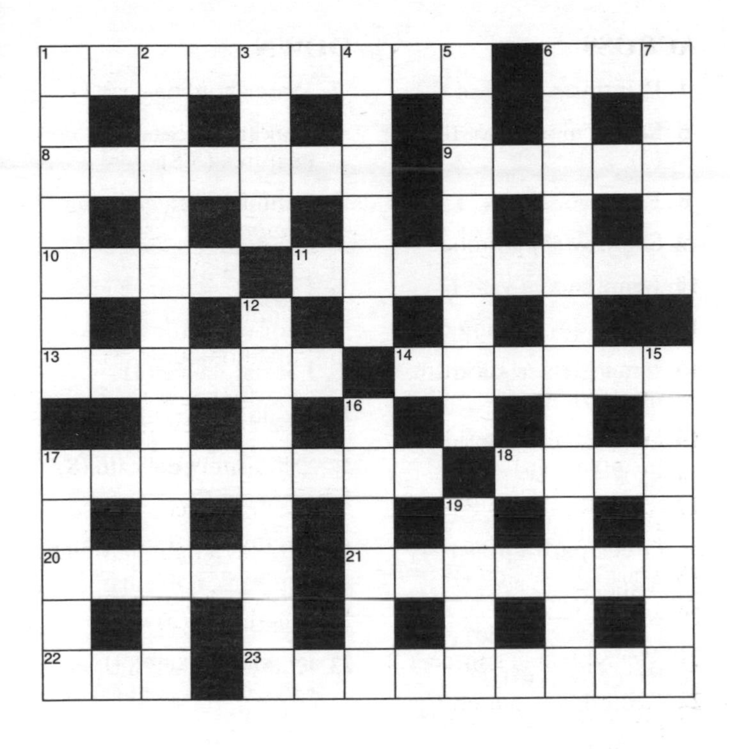
1
2
3
4
5
6
7
8
9
10
11
12
13
14
15
16
17
18
19
20
21
22
23

ACROSS

1 Free-form effusion (8)

5 Study (university subject) (4)

9 Triple godhead (7)

10 Copying (5)

11 Jump; sort of year (4)

12 School (7)

14 It made Beerbohm insufferable (6)

16 Water-boiler (6)

19 Sink, fail (7)

21 Roman Catholic head; Greek parish priest (4)

24 Adhere; cane (5)

25 Contravene (rule) (7)

26 Rather wet (4)

27 One MP does not fear losing (4,4)

DOWN

1 Duty list (4)

2 Live (especially *with me*) (5)

3 A butterfly; a captain (7)

4 Solid carbon dioxide (3,3)

6 Urgent, pressing (7)

7 Poor verse (8)

8 Formal dance (4)

13 Muddled up (8)

15 School of e.g. Matisse (7)

17 Blow up (7)

18 Unimportant facts (6)

20 Top-rank nobleman (4)

22 Tranquillity (5)

23 Hamlet wished his *too-solid flesh* would (4)

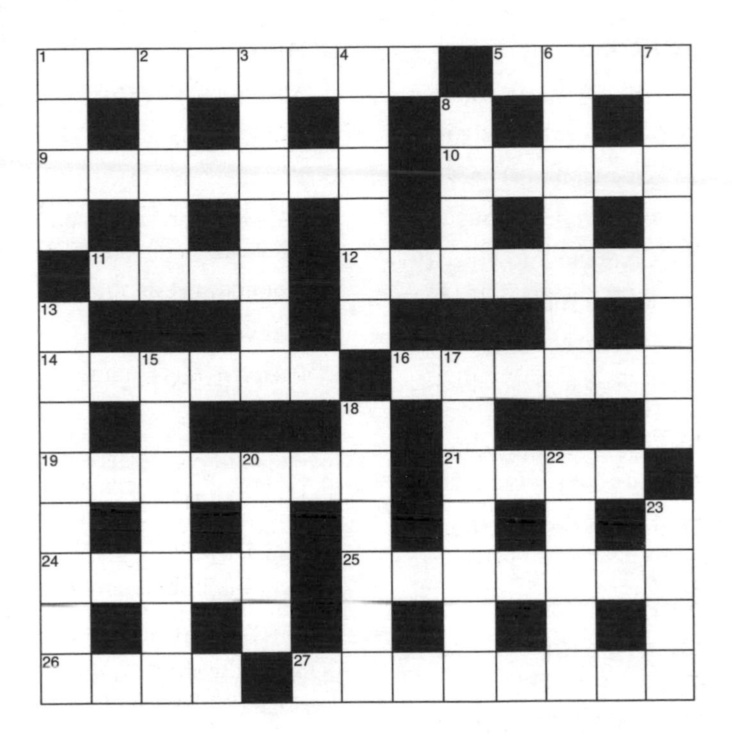

ACROSS

1 Drinking vessel (6)

4 One keeping tally (6)

8 Tree-trunk (4)

9 Bothered; anxious (8)

10 Combine into unity (9)

13 Recess for statue (5)

15 Portion (of cake) (5)

16 Part of body; piece of furniture (5)

18 Aus. monolith; *corker, say (anagram)* (5,4)

21 End of the line (8)

22 Watch-face (4)

23 Plump (6)

24 A cure (6)

DOWN

1 Malicious fairy (6)

2 Demean (8)

3 Private coach (5)

5 Vulgarity; undeveloped state (9)

6 Get under skin of (4)

7 Make smaller (6)

11 Period of development (9)

12 Similar (5)

14 George IV's queen (8)

16 Little Bighorn his last stand (6)

17 Thin gruel (6)

19 Vertical part of stair (5)

20 Be worried; fingerboard ridge (4)

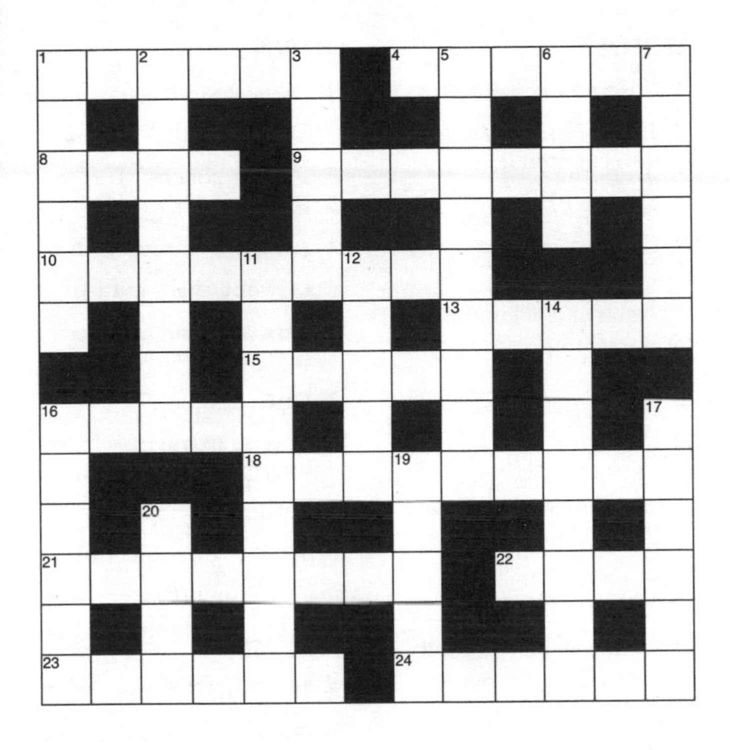

ACROSS

1 Aircraft engine cover (7)

5 Beam-bouncing detection method (5)

8 Bundle of corn (5)

9 (Disease) native to area (7)

10 An artificial language (9)

12 Sharp cutter (3)

13 Clergyman (6)

14 Protective clothes, have strings (6)

17 A constellation; various Popes (3)

18 In love; Titania was, *of an ass* (9)

20 Location; place of duty; post (7)

21 Feathered weapon (5)

23 Bring to bear (effort, pressure) (5)

24 Shake (7)

DOWN

1 (Hereditary) layer of society (5)

2 Misery (3)

3 Raging fire (7)

4 An elopers' Green (6)

5 Cowboy show (5)

6 Personal manner, bearing (9)

7 Dins; a game (7)

11 Vote in name of (another) (9)

13 Fur-lined cloak (7)

15 Secular; disrespectful to religion (7)

16 A gemstone; sounds like an Alf (6)

18 Turn out of home (5)

19 Use rod to find water (5)

22 To chafe (3)

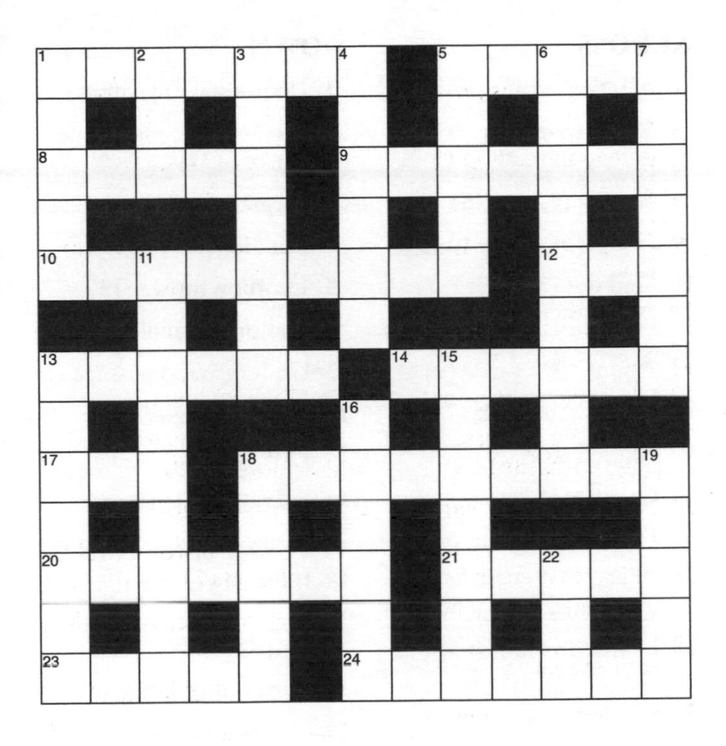
1
2
3
4
5
6
7
8
9
10
11
12
13
14
15
16
17
18
19
20
21
22
23
24

ACROSS

1 A lot of (4)

3 Vivid; type of arts (7)

8 Powdery woodcutting residue (7)

9 Joyful (5)

10 Find out (5)

11 French bean (7)

13 About 1092 yards (9)

17 Goods sent back (7)

19 Hidden store (5)

20 Celebrated (5)

22 French city, papal palace (7)

23 One under instruction (7)

24 Learned volume (4)

DOWN

1 Body tissue; strength (6)

2 Racecourse; card game (9)

3 Clearly understand (3,3,7)

4 Loathe (5)

5 Jump on one leg (3)

6 The prairie wolf (6)

7 Underground passage (6)

12 A loudening of sound (9)

14 Ploy (6)

15 Advantage (6)

16 Session with medium (6)

18 Inert gas, element 86 (5)

21 New Zealand extinct bird (3)

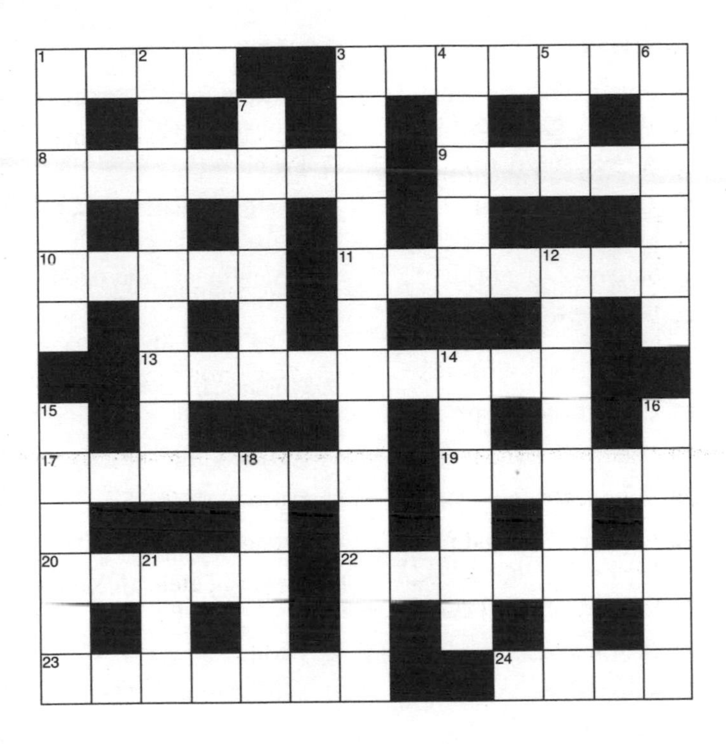
1
2
3
4
5
6
7
8
9
10
11
12
13
14
15
16
17
18
19
20
21
22
23
24

ACROSS

1 Competence to get around (8)

5 A tie; a surety (4)

8 The Mystery Cat (*T. S. Eliot*) (8)

9 Summon; ring (4)

11 Is it still for tea? (*Brooke – Grantchester*) (5)

12 E.g. gas, water supplier (7)

13 Grief (6)

15 (Face) showing distress (6)

18 Socks, stockings etc. (7)

19 Item of information (5)

21 Civil wrong (4)

22 Material used to fill (8)

23 Caution, care (4)

24 Streaked with grey (8)

DOWN

1 Ancient Egypt capital; Tennessee port (7)

2 Pig meat (5)

3 Revoltingly affectionate (5-5)

4 Disapproval expression (3-3)

6 Delirious applause (7)

7 Hold up; hang back (5)

10 *We're off to see* him (Garland film) (6,2,2)

14 Earmark; spare (7)

16 Super-human hero (7)

17 Mollusc, eaten by Walrus and Carpenter (6)

18 Tie up; a snag (5)

20 Judicial process (5)

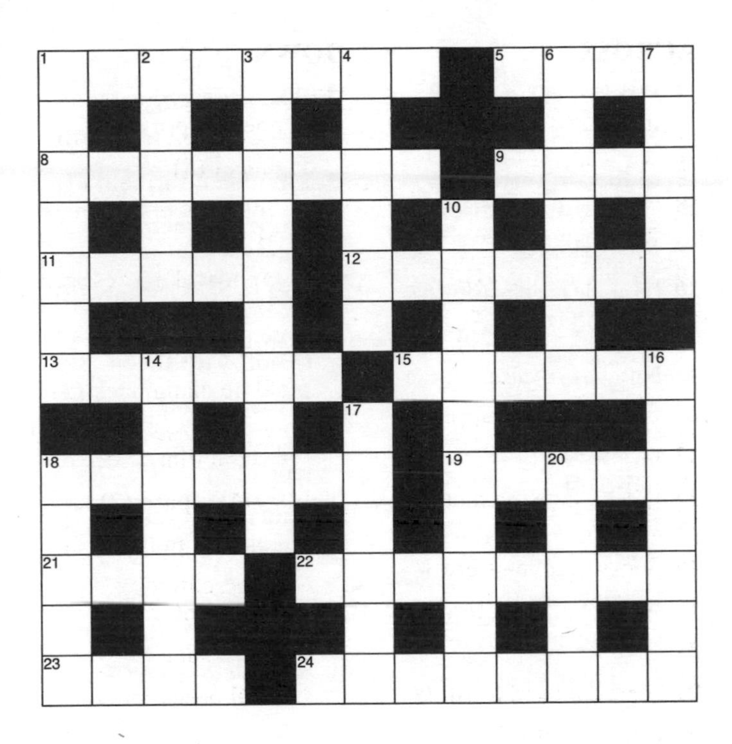
1
2
3
4
5
6
7
8
9
10
11
12
13
14
15
16
17
18
19
20
21
22
23
24

ACROSS

3 Friendly (8)

7 Nicked (6)

8 In the air; very quick (visit) (6)

9 Rich cake (6)

10 (Female) seclusion (6)

11 Knight's attendant (4)

13 Number of *cards* in the *trick* (5)

15 Young woman (4)

17 Eerie (6)

18 Sharpness (of intellect) (6)

19 Deed; battle (6)

20 Overweening pride (6)

21 Song of lament for the dead (8)

DOWN

1 Rock layers (6)

2 Bring charge (that) (6)

3 Emotional torment (7)

4 Work together (to deceive) (7)

5 Port in heel of Italy (8)

6 Type of porcelain; (paint) with sheen (8)

11 Liking, inclination (8)

12 Energetic, self-made type (2-6)

13 China seas cyclone (7)

14 Instinctive fellow-feeling (7)

15 Soiled, dirty (6)

16 Keep in possession (6)

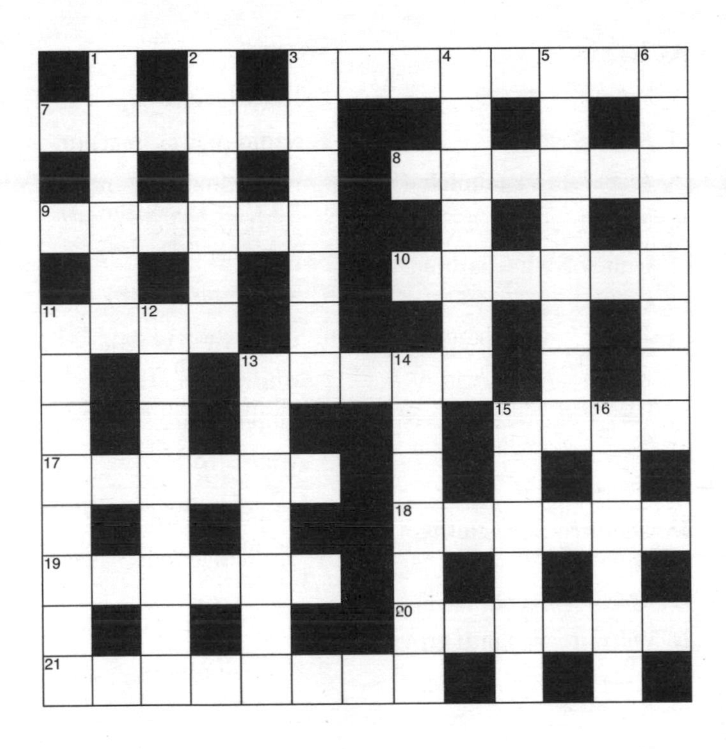

ACROSS

1 Violate code (10)

8 Ambushed (7)

9 A spread; an adhesive (5)

10 Disastrous defeat (4)

11 Uninvolved; separate (8)

13 Stoneworker (5)

14 Kingsley Amis's *Lucky Jim* – (5)

16 Very wet; fat from roast (8)

17 Twosome (4)

20 Colourful seed-eating songbird (5)

21 Concealing (7)

22 Wiltshire megalith group (10)

DOWN

1 Tall structure (5)

2 Radio panel discussion (3,9)

3 An East European (4)

4 Steering device (6)

5 A Spanish Jew (8)

6 Suffocation (12)

7 Muffle (sound) (6)

12 Simple photo (8)

13 Adjust (6)

15 Irregular, not smooth (6)

18 Scoundrel; mad elephant (5)

19 Desire (4)

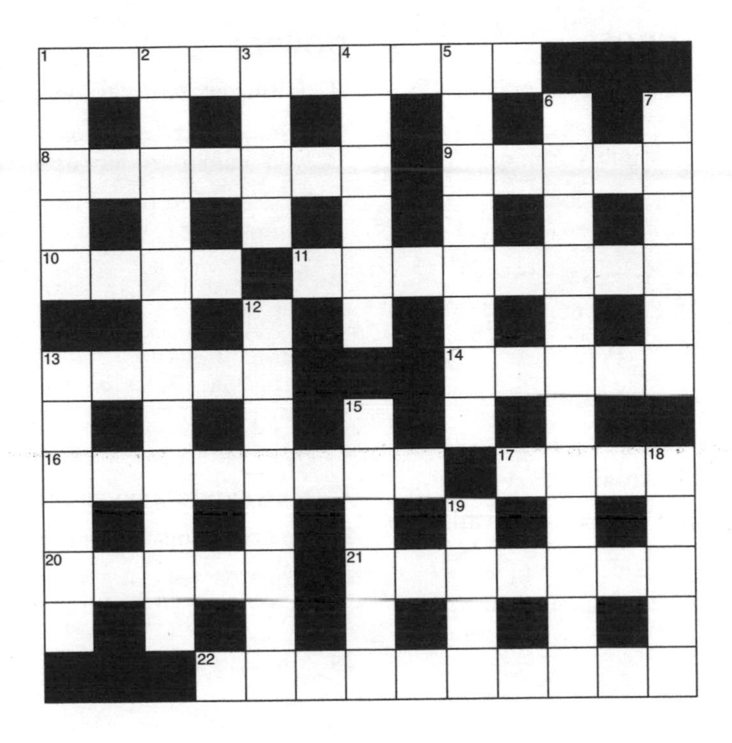

ACROSS

1 Contribute opinion (4,4,3)

7 Military trumpet (5)

8 Hero's lover (*Much Ado about Nothing*) (7)

10 Repair, restore (8)

11 Feeble person (4)

13 Response (6)

15 Soapy froth (6)

17 One engaging eye (4)

18 Hawaii capital (8)

21 More prepared (7)

22 Sight; part of play (5)

23 Afternoon off (4-7)

DOWN

1 Sewing accessory dealer (11)

2 Non-animal-product user (5)

3 Summary (8)

4 Arouse (6)

5 Kill (4)

6 German/Jewish vernacular (7)

9 At advantageous time (11)

12 Noisy drinking bout (8)

14 An organ; to tolerate (7)

16 A quarter (6)

19 Tip over (5)

20 A beak; a statement (4)

ACROSS

1 Quibble (5)

7 Principled (7)

8 Woodblock (floor) (7)

9 Ham it up (7)

11 Saturate (6)

13 Restless desire (for) (9)

15 US Western film tough-guy (4,5)

19 Hearty laugh (6)

21 Prohibits (7)

23 Variant of element (7)

24 Reticule; Jack Worthing mislaid in one (7)

25 Call across Swiss valley (5)

DOWN

1 Love god (5)

2 Engulfing spiral (e.g. of whirlpool) (6)

3 Get (project) started (6)

4 Ban (4)

5 Looking-glass (6)

6 Railed platform; theatre area (7)

10 Norse raider; a sea area (6)

12 Risk, danger (6)

14 Washington DC river (7)

16 A nonentity; Pooter, for Grossmiths (6)

17 Speech of praise (6)

18 Provide; be able to purchase (6)

20 Execute turning movement (5)

22 Breathy gesture; the *Moor's Last*, Rushdie (4)

ACROSS

1 Tolerating (8)

5 Mound (4)

8 Castle mound (5)

9 *Onegin, Godunov* poet (7)

11 Chance; large amount (3)

12 An indigenous person (9)

13 Given name, new soundtrack (6)

15 One having to live abroad (6)

18 One taking the blame (9)

19 Hostelry (3)

20 (Look) sideways, disapprovingly (7)

21 Diver's breathing pack (5)

22 Speck; as opposed to *beam* (4)

23 Good-looking (8)

DOWN

1 Was clumsily inefficient (7)

2 Work for eight (5)

3 Mildly supervise (4,2,3,2)

4 Japan, for Japanese (6)

6 Vague notion (7)

7 Thrust forward (5)

10 Branded as bad (11)

14 Bed covering; comprehensive (7)

16 Hug (7)

17 Nine-day prayer cycle (6)

18 Throng; climb (up) (5)

19 Outermost planet (5)

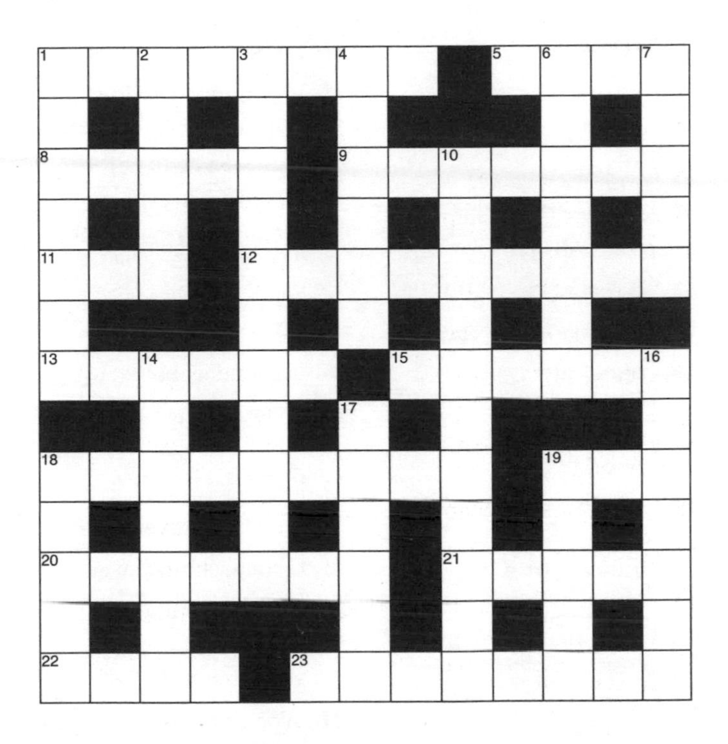

ACROSS

1 Tube; whistle (4)

3 Minor medical attention (5,3)

9 Hoarder of money (5)

10 Intention, aim (7)

11 To revel (7)

12 One hunted for food (4)

14 Genial (6)

16 Edible grain (6)

18 Sand drift (4)

19 Complete circuit (*baseball*) (4,3)

22 Briefings with the latest (7)

23 Crush, break violently (5)

24 In youthful way (8)

25 Norse thunder god (4)

DOWN

1 Welsh town; Oxford, Cambridge college (8)

2 Fourteen days before Easter (7,6)

4 Meaning; bring from abroad (6)

5 Tiny weight; moral doubt (7)

6 Unimpeachable (5,8)

7 Food regime; a parliament (4)

8 Badly-behaved child (4)

13 Decisive argument (8)

15 Ophelia's brother (7)

17 Wood-working tool (6)

20 Pressed grape juice; a necessity (4)

21 Type of plant; one giving light (4)

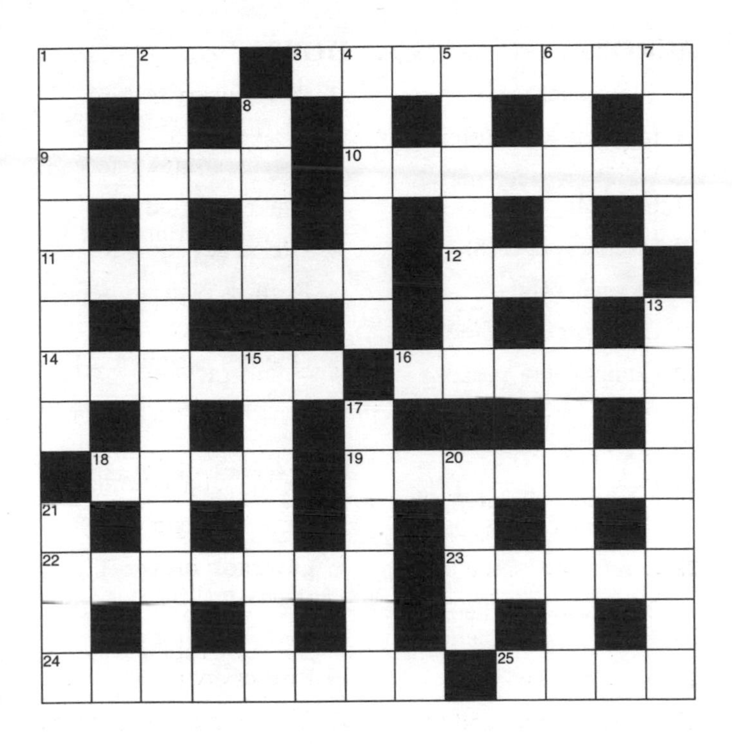

ACROSS

4 Soothsayer (5)

7 Impractically idealistic (8)

8 Water creature; metal plate (4)

9 Suicide (pilot) (8)

10 Rugged, solid (6)

13 Elephant driver (6)

14 Complaining, parrot, noise (6)

15 Highest point (6)

18 Pass, move across (8)

19 Look sullen, alluring (4)

20 Large bottle (8)

21 Beneficiary of cheque (5)

DOWN

1 Cross eyes (6)

2 Plucked-string instrument (6)

3 Unemphasised (3-3)

4 Excite, get going (8)

5 Restless pleasure-seeker (8)

6 One not accepted (6)

11 In unserviceable fashion (8)

12 A school; disadvantage (8)

14 (Persian) provincial governor; *as part (anagram)* (6)

15 *Aeneid* author (6)

16 Bird of prey (6)

17 Of horses (6)

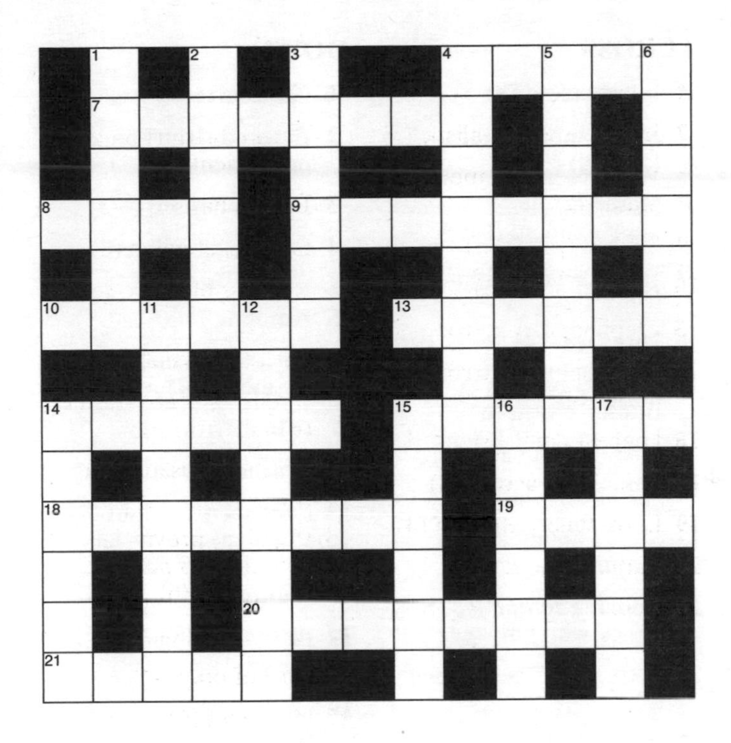

ACROSS

1 Improvident (8)

7 Swim; apply water to (wound) (5)

8 Order, act of imprisonment (9)

9 White wine/cassis drink (3)

10 Pare; neat (4)

11 Take away; Billy Bunter's form (6)

13 Missing company (6)

14 A football club; a suit (6)

17 Knock about; a food coating (6)

18 Rough attempt; attack with knife (4)

20 A tree; sounds like *pelt* (3)

22 Remiss (9)

23 T. S. –, poet (5)

24 Intensify (8)

DOWN

1 Gem surface (5)

2 A perennial; Thomas –, poet/composer (7)

3 Beast's den (4)

4 One being painted; easy catch (6)

5 Amount bet (5)

6 Push down; make miserable (7)

7 A bad error; a loaf (7)

12 Brazenly overt (7)

13 Published handout (7)

15 Go back; a nook (7)

16 Scanty (6)

17 Plait; edge band of e.g. silk (5)

19 One passed on in relay race (5)

21 Ruler; a chessman (4)

1
2
3
4
5
6
7
8
9
10
11
12
13
14
15
16
17
18
19
20
21
22
23
24

ACROSS

1 Tomahawk (7)

5 Unfocused sight (4)

9 Maintain right to (5)

10 Boasted (7)

11 Wearer of the Scarlet Letter (*Hawthorne*) (6,6)

12 Proverb (6)

13 Population count (6)

16 Teacher; *the classroom (anagram)* (12)

19 Exact opposite (7)

20 Put into coordination (5)

21 Number of tails, lives, of cat (4)

22 Lucerne plant (7)

DOWN

1 A wine; pawn (4)

2 Bad-end play (7)

3 Wolsey's London palace (7,5)

4 Alehouse (6)

6 Romance-language parent (5)

7 Richard –, *South Pacific* composer (7)

8 Six-foot-pole weapon (12)

12 Court, parliament, meeting (7)

14 Out of the ordinary (7)

15 Shape-changing protozoan (6)

17 Place of refuge (5)

18 Old Peruvian (4)

1
2
3
4
5
6
7
8
9
10
11
12
13
14
15
16
17
18
19
20
21
22

ACROSS

1 Conceal; skin (4)

3 Typical example (8)

8 Lateral part (4)

9 Rules expressed in symbols (*maths.*) (8)

11 Trickery; conjuror's incantation (5-5)

14 Courage; ghost (6)

15 Give satisfaction to (6)

17 Sea-plane (6,4)

20 Put a name to (8)

21 Reasonable; light-coloured (4)

22 (Inscription) on stone (8)

23 Head growth (4)

DOWN

1 Not to be talked about (4-4)

2 Imparting a lesson (8)

4 Particle of light (6)

5 Protective colouring, concealment (10)

6 A grinder (4)

7 Scottish turnip (4)

10 Swung from side to side (10)

12 Wide view (8)

13 University teacher (8)

16 Not be the same (6)

18 Satiate; wholly occupy (4)

19 (Liquid) trickle thinly (4)

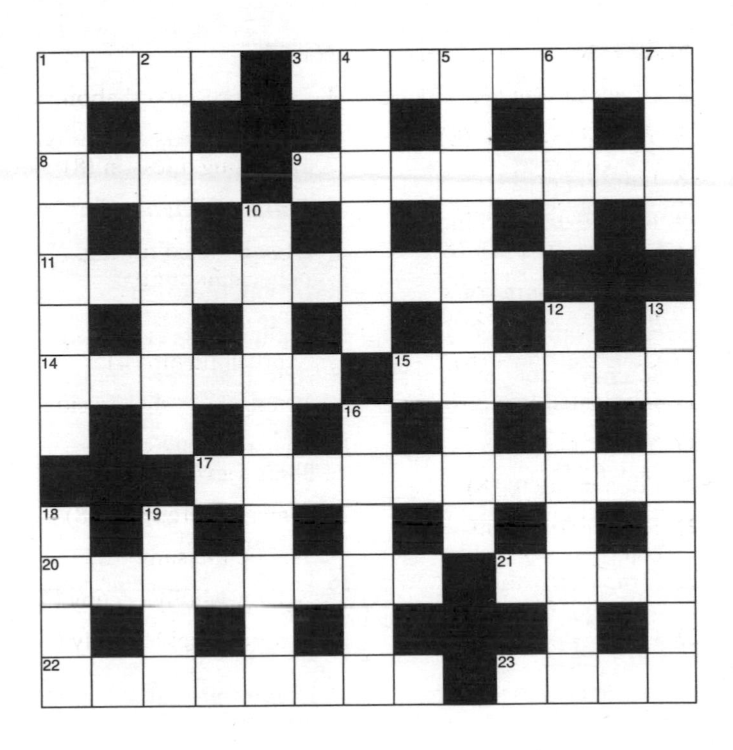
1
2
3
4
5
6
7
8
9
10
11
12
13
14
15
16
17
18
19
20
21
22
23

ACROSS

1 Of education; pedantic (10)

8 One chasing (7)

9 Fraction of pound (5)

10 Cage for hen (4)

11 Keeping apart (8)

13 Pound with fists (6)

15 Potential; not yet manifested (6)

17 (Especially pre-Lent) festivity (8)

18 Collection of data; rasp (4)

21 A raptor; two-under score (5)

22 Lover of Cressida (7)

23 Seeing how far one can go (6,2,2)

DOWN

2 Freight (5)

3 Burden of responsibility (4)

4 Skilful (6)

5 Of equatorial regions (8)

6 1/100th franc (7)

7 Feeling no gravity (10)

8 Artful Dodger's trade (*Dickens*) (10)

12 Style of speaking; liberation (8)

14 Husband of one's dreams (2,5)

16 Package; *Two Cities* hero (*Dickens*) (6)

19 Ice house (5)

20 Hindu spiritual master; cartoon bear (4)

1
2
3
4
5
6
7
8
9
10
11
12
13
14
15
16
17
18
19
20
21
22
23

ACROSS

1 (Caught) in the act (3-6)

6 Lorry (*abbr.*) (1,1,1)

8 Bar door to (strikers) (4,3)

9 Bedroom at sea (5)

10 Cog-engaging lever (4)

11 (Water)birds one shoots (8)

13 Surviving (6)

14 Agreement; a trade union (6)

17 Without warning (8)

18 G. B. —, Irish dramatist (4)

20 In bad temper (5)

21 Communion cup (7)

22 Serious personal injury (*abbr.*) (1,1,1)

23 Traditional cuddly toy (5,4)

DOWN

1 Return to the bad (7)

2 Take suicidal risk (4,4,5)

3 Boat-hailing call (4)

4 Small particular (6)

5 In moral, artistic decline (8)

6 Only one to pick from (7,6)

7 Open to bribes (5)

12 Lewd (8)

15 January 1st its Day (3,4)

16 Unruffled (6)

17 Hurl; arm support (5)

19 Shy of effort (4)

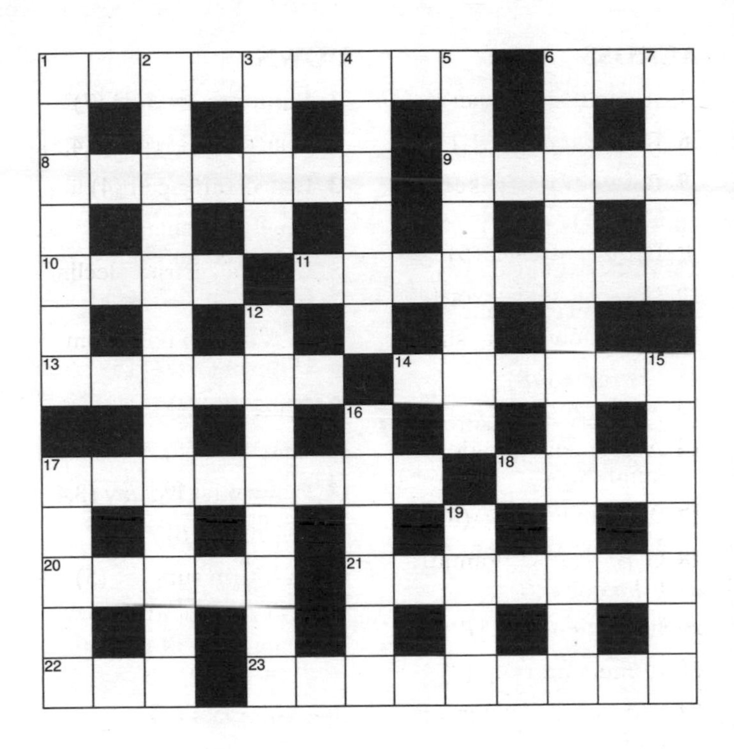

ACROSS

7 Avoid (capture) (5)
8 Rust away (7)
9 Clown (7)
10 A line dance (5)
11 Work over again (4)
12 Clearance; (at one's) discretion (8)
15 Corrupted (8)
16 Old Tory opponent (4)
19 Causing death (5)
21 Shorten (text) (7)
22 Inexplicable event (7)
23 Map book (5)

DOWN

1 Limb; one in club (6)
2 Conceited; inflated (6,2)
3 One diverting attention (5)
4 Rule, maxim (7)
5 Complain; low wind sound (4)
6 Happen (*arch.*) (6)
8 Polite, thoughtful (11)
13 Timetable (8)
14 William –, led Scots against Edward I (7)
15 To libel (6)
17 Slippery, fatty (6)
18 Snap; piece of good luck in career (5)
20 Lawn grass (4)

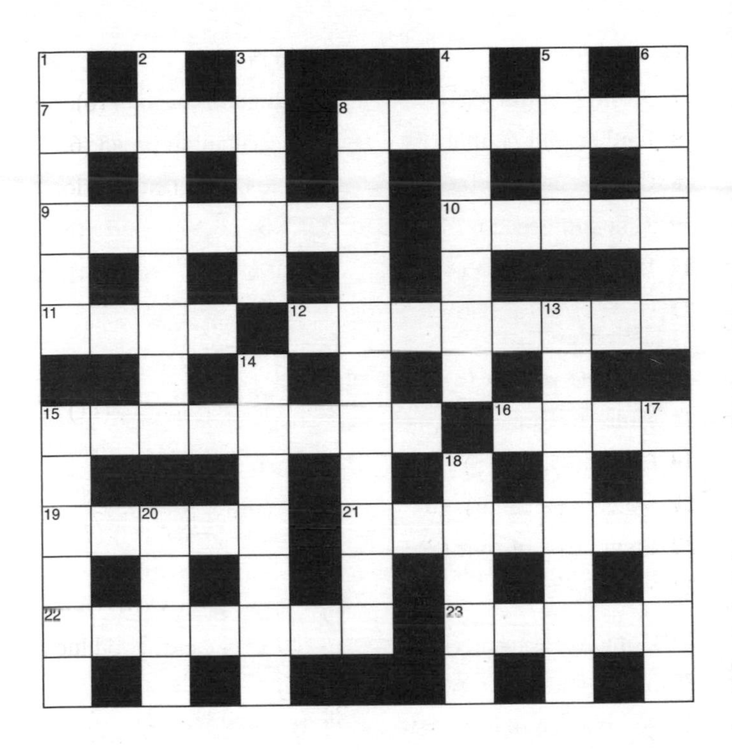
1
2
3
4
5
6
7
8
9
10
11
12
13
14
15
16
17
18
19
20
21
22
23

ACROSS

1 Stern; forceful (4)

4 Unthankful people (8)

8 Promiscuous women (8)

9 Take long strides (4)

10 US president after Washington (5)

11 25th March (4,3)

13 Illegible writing (6)

15 Hole (to thread cord) (6)

18 Fine glass (7)

20 Country of Sphinx (5)

23 Some lines of text; type of soldier (*both abbrs.*) (4)

24 Compass housing (8)

25 Sweet-smelling (8)

26 Ancient small harp (4)

DOWN

2 Pungent; caustic (5)

3 Unpalatable choice (7)

4 Press; an element (4)

5 Cobweb; fine gauze (8)

6 Put at rest (suspicion) (5)

7 Atone for (7)

10 Fathead (3)

12 Moorish palace, Granada (8)

14 Barbary pirate (7)

16 Decorate with notches; *realign (anagram)* (7)

17 Shoddy stuff (3)

19 Jargon (5)

21 Of the highest latitudes (5)

22 Biting little insect (4)

ACROSS

1 A tax; unavoidable task (4)

3 Ban (8)

8 Distinctive clothes (4)

9 Sting-in-tail creature (8)

11 Wooden spoon (5,5)

14 Gloomy, depressing (6)

15 In poor health (6)

17 Courtly-love singer (10)

20 One of ruling clique (8)

21 Manifestation (4)

22 Writer of short pieces (8)

23 Over-the-top publicity (4)

DOWN

1 A menial drudge (8)

2 Slowcoach; Mock Turtle's teacher (*Alice*) (8)

4 Officially write down (6)

5 Lying flat (10)

6 Morsel as lure (4)

7 Melody (4)

10 *Pygmalion* musical (2,4,4)

12 Savage violence (8)

13 Italian city; loving sister of Dombey (Son) (8)

16 Liquid secretions (6)

18 Prod; old bonnet (4)

19 Sound of static, of disapproval (4)

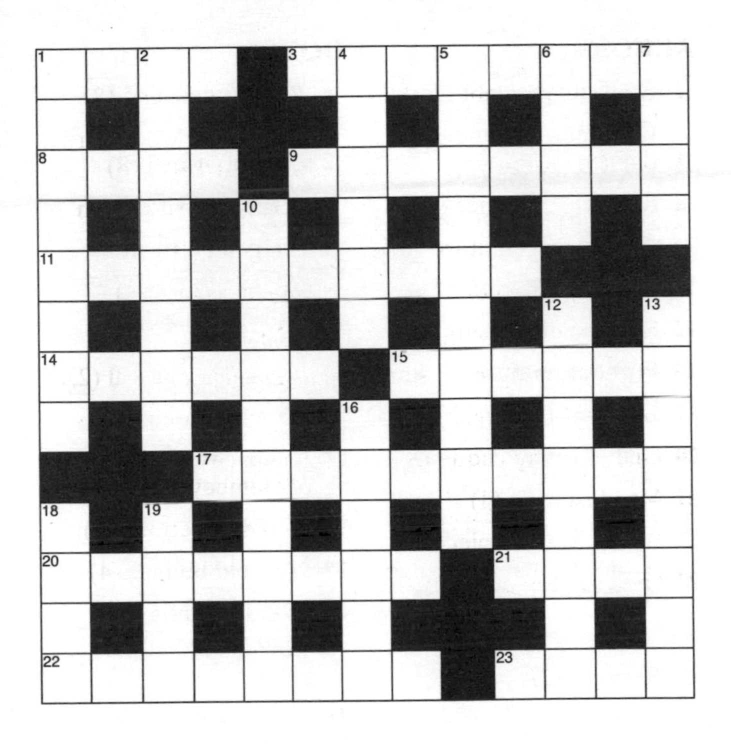

ACROSS

1 Radically severe (7)

5 Chairman's hammer (5)

8 Dryly amusing (5)

9 Real surname of Lenin (7)

10 Holiness (8)

11 Shivering fit (4)

13 Without restraint (2,5,6)

16 Bombast (4)

17 Badly wounded, ravaged (8)

20 Remark, observation (7)

21 Real surname of George Eliot (5)

22 Quiz team (5)

23 Rapture (7)

DOWN

1 Real surname of Lewis Carroll (7)

2 Fruit of oak (5)

3 A sneak (8)

4 Prefix used by noble's heir (8,5)

5 Teases; opposite of *Dolls* (4)

6 Acetic-acid preservative (7)

7 Court reception; US embankment (5)

12 Caution (8)

14 Executioner (7)

15 Line of kings (7)

16 Cover main points again (5)

18 Eucalyptus-eating marsupial (5)

19 Pseudonym of Brontës (4)

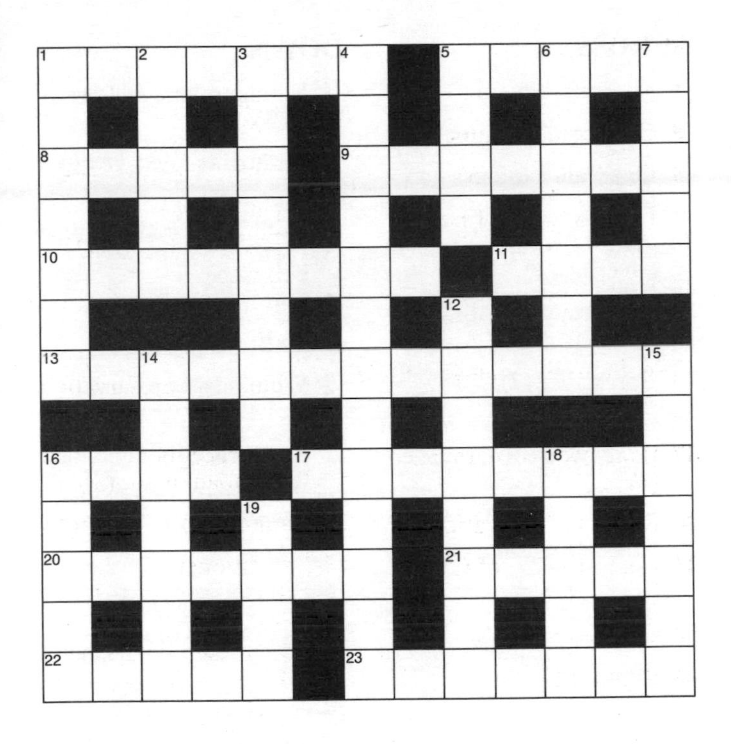

ACROSS

5 Tiny width (5-7)

8 Beam over door (6)

9 Overpaid businessman (3,3)

10 Piece of roof, floor covering (4)

12 Gracefully slim, like a tree (7)

14 Contradict (7)

15 Cut, carved with effort (4)

17 Eremite (6)

18 Capital of Canada (6)

20 Fates; *Macbeth* witches (5,7)

DOWN

1 Stocking-hanging time (9,3)

2 Shaft; one is *backed* to it (4)

3 Commerce; road vehicles (7)

4 Old Paris prison (8)

6 To brood (4)

7 What a lying excuse! (4,4,4)

11 Place-identifying feature (8)

13 Dream; genre of fiction (7)

16 Failure; damage (4)

19 Opponents of *us* (4)

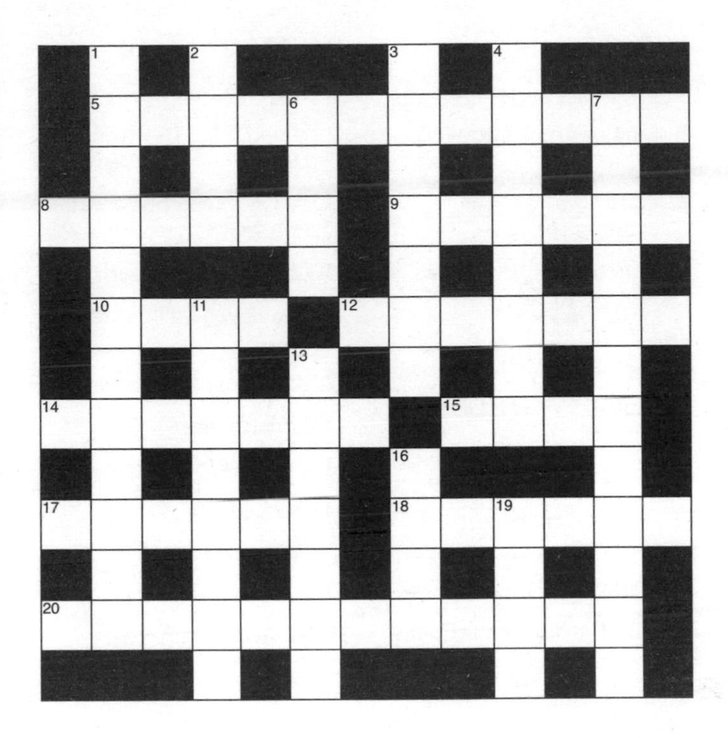
1
2
3
4
5
6
7
8
9
10
11
12
13
14
15
16
17
18
19
20

ACROSS

2 Aware; level-headed (8)

6 One of great knowledge (6)

8 Hard to make out; cunning (6)

9 Vegetable; one Walrus wanted to discuss (*Carroll*) (7)

10 Cancel; waste (5)

12 Kingsley novel; Devon town (8,2)

16 Ali Baba's spell (4,6)

18 Swiss-German border river (5)

20 Madman (7)

21 Hired group of clappers (6)

22 Start (journey); display, explain (3,3)

23 All of us (8)

DOWN

1 Low wall on roof (7)

2 Be still, fail to progress (8)

3 A US vegetable; a game (6)

4 One snapping teeth (5)

5 Privileged to be omitted (6)

7 Keenness to advance (8)

11 Unvarying (8)

13 Conceal (8)

14 Wicked (7)

15 Baby nursery (6)

17 Poverty (6)

19 Mental picture (5)

ACROSS

1 Berkshire racecourse (5)

4 Restricted (7)

8 Raise to peerage (7)

9 Praise highly (5)

10 Appointment book (5)

11 Get hold of (6)

13 One or the other (6)

15 Allay (6)

18 Excavate (stone); one hunted (6)

20 Welsh town; something hard, igniting (5)

22 Deposit; take accommodation (5)

23 Made void; denied (7)

24 (Spaceship's) return to atmosphere (2-5)

25 Belated, slow (5)

DOWN

1 The Granite City (8)

2 State of touching; useful acquaintance (7)

3 Rather fat (5)

4 Avoid attention (3,3)

5 Star conductor (7)

6 Everyone play (*music*) (5)

7 Dish out; a benefit (4)

12 (Argued) in emotional way (8)

14 Pledge; serious (7)

16 A cheat; (US) whirlwind (7)

17 New South Wales capital (6)

19 Excessive (5)

20 Battle (5)

21 Pronounce indistinctly (4)

ACROSS

1 Encroach (8)

5 Safety device; melt together (4)

7 Smelling salts (3,8)

8 Mercy, sympathy (4)

9 Move in from margin; place order (6)

10 Mafia conspiracy of silence (6)

13 Small hotel (3)

14 City of ancient Greece, Egypt (6)

17 Mass departure (6)

18 Narrow opening; gashed (4)

19 Bravura performance (4,2,5)

20 A bird; it flies straight (4)

21 Speak condescendingly; help pilot's descent (4,4)

DOWN

1 Vow-of-silence monk (8)

2 Totter; influence (4)

3 A commercial (13)

4 Makes pact with devil (5,4,4)

5 (Fine) condition (6)

6 Pick; specially picked (6)

7 Heavy pudding (6)

11 Poser; sieve (6)

12 German shepherd (8)

15 Virtue; a top card (6)

16 Underground lair; dig this (6)

18 Race along (clouds) (4)

ACROSS

7 Honest; accurate (4)

8 Come close to (8)

9 Prolific (6)

10 Symbol, badge (6)

11 Worthless, deplorable (4)

12 Construct anew (2-6)

15 Break (regulation) (8)

17 Avoid (question, bouncer) (4)

18 Treeless permafrost zone (6)

21 With eagerness (6)

22 A brew (8)

23 Stake; position (held) (4)

DOWN

1 One from Erevan (8)

2 Rubbish; decline (6)

3 Senior bureaucrat; type of 17 *ac* (8)

4 Domed recess in church (4)

5 Much more; a lookalike (6)

6 Dull pain (4)

13 Halting; verifying (8)

14 Tricky (problem); easily made to laugh (8)

16 Element 88, discovered by Curies (6)

17 A French Channel port (6)

19 Longer forearm bone (4)

20 Related, similar (4)

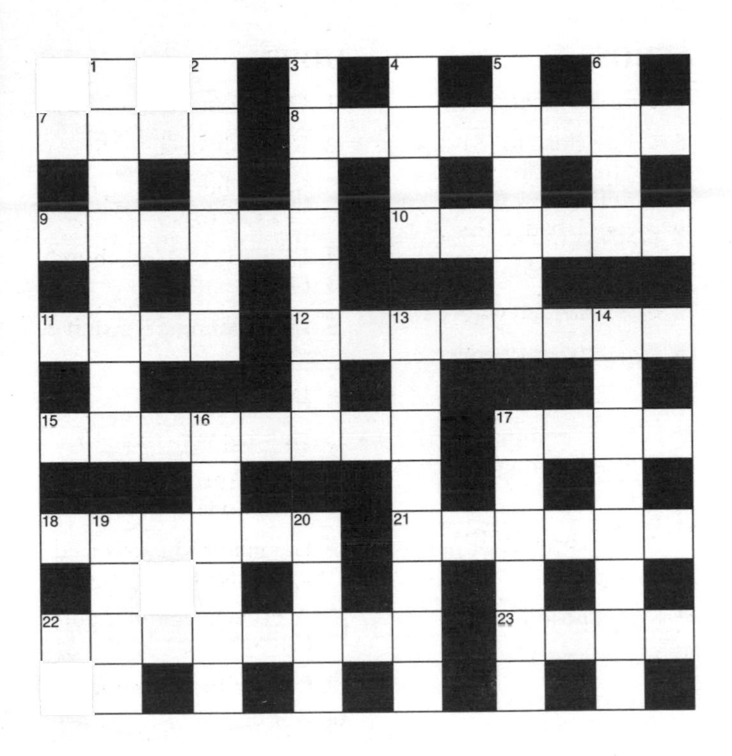

ACROSS

1 Four kings; a sweet flower (7)

5 Seating enclosure; resolute view (5)

8 Four-point ball (snooker) (5)

9 Manx town; type of fir (7)

10 Fruit; rude noise (9)

12 Mesh; fly-trap (3)

13 A spice; red (hair) (6)

14 Disordered mess (6)

17 Robert E. –, Confederate commander (3)

18 Decorum (9)

20 Made fizzy (7)

21 One bit of sand; wood texture (5)

23 Eight kings; unit of inductance (5)

24 Fugitives (7)

DOWN

1 Carl Maria von –, *Freischütz* composer (5)

2 Card game, a stake in it (3)

3 Base, unworthy (7)

4 Up to date (6)

5 Improper; impertinent (5)

6 Licit (9)

7 Put out of action (7)

11 New Testament Jewish council; *has dinner (anagram)* (9)

13 Giant David killed (7)

15 Honest; on one's feet (7)

16 Haiti cult, spell (6)

18 Short and sharp (5)

19 A long time (*informal*) (5)

22 Ottoman commander (3)

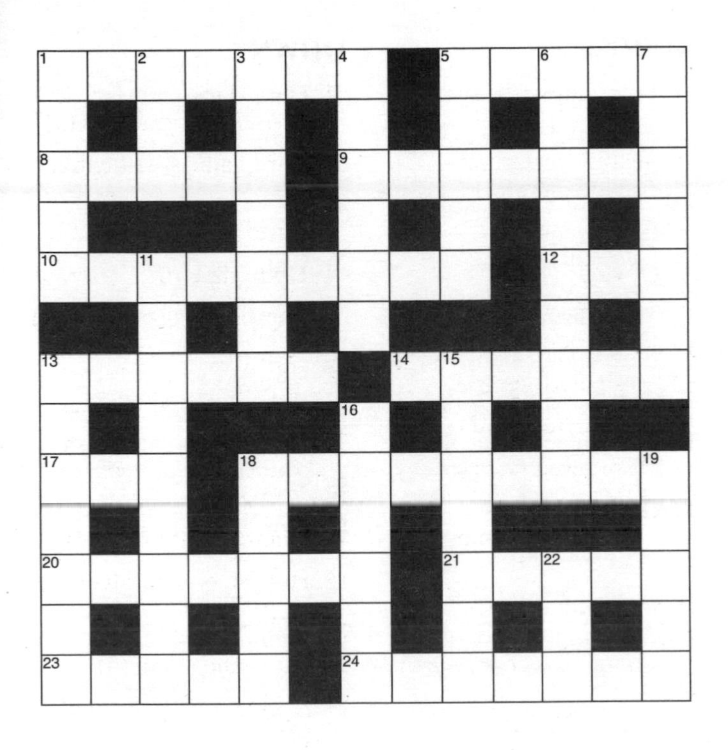

ACROSS

1 Promotion of kin (8)

5 Part of leg; baby animal (4)

9 Suspension of hostilities (5)

10 Obvious (7)

11 That which is left over (7)

12 Barbarian tribesmen (5)

13 Getting bald (4,2,3)

18 Challenging behaviour (5)

20 Offer; resist (4,3)

22 Warning; wariness (7)

23 Surface lustre (5)

24 Cleopatra its serpent (*Antony and Cleopatra*) (4)

25 Get together (8)

DOWN

1 Oath-giving official (6)

2 Drop like stone (7)

3 Greek *th* (5)

4 Amorous burble (5,8)

6 Watchful (5)

7 One irrationally worshipped (6)

8 Dwarf (6)

14 Humorously incongruous (6)

15 Saw (7)

16 French chorus-line dance (6)

17 Position, attitude (6)

19 Thin porridge (5)

21 Strong cotton fabric (5)

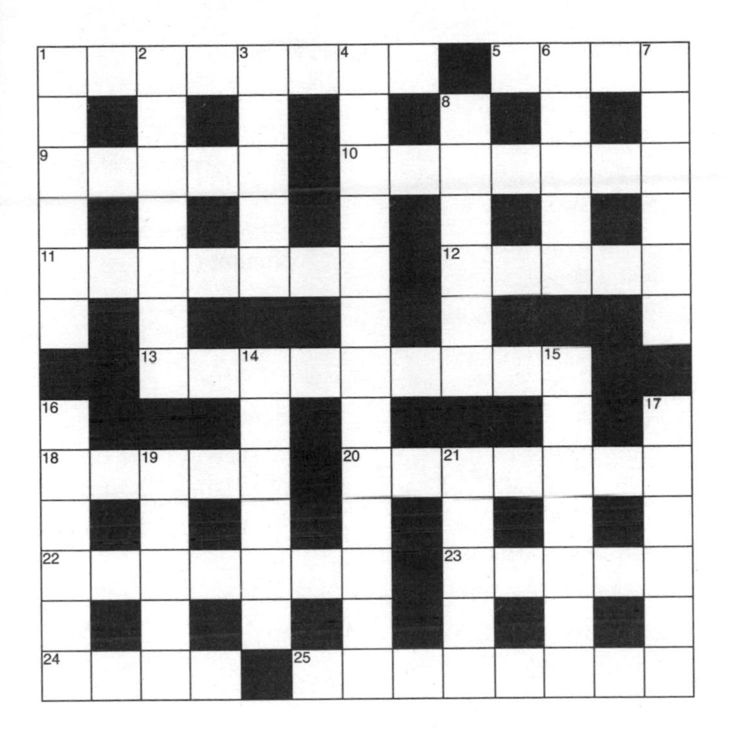

ACROSS

1 Permission; penalty (8)

5 Stylish (4)

9 Edible bulb; sounds like *Tennyson's Lady* (7)

10 Instrument, in cinema once (5)

11 Unable to move; able to speed (4)

12 Country home (7)

14 "Wilco" (navy) (3,3); lemur-like primate (3-3)

16 Bring to conclusion; prepare (e.g. toy) to start (4,2)

19 The tallest mammal (7)

21 Something owed (4)

24 Teller of life's tale (*Macbeth*) (5)

25 Type of reed Moses was found in (7)

26 A foodstuff; as sure as — is — (4)

27 A drink; *teenager (anagram)* (5,3)

DOWN

1 Neither good nor bad (2-2)

2 Spiral-horned antelope (5)

3 Creator of Anna Karenina (7)

4 Science of light, sight (6)

6 Gaunt; a captured hawk (7)

7 Derision (8)

8 Make secure; race off (4)

13 Optimistic; florid (8)

15 Deserving, receiving (7)

17 Gratify; pamper (7)

18 North African Muslim people, language (6)

20 Is just right; convulsions (4)

22 Pointed (remark); (blade) not sharp (5)

23 Flightless bird; Saturn satellite (4)

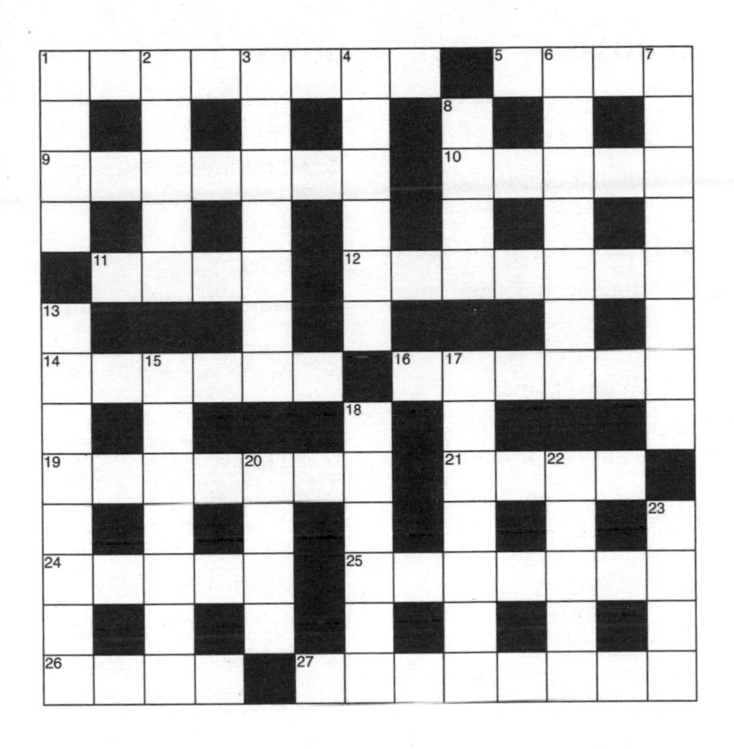
1
2
3
4
5
6
7
8
9
10
11
12
13
14
15
16
17
18
19
20
21
22
23
24
25
26
27

ACROSS

1 A covering, awning (6)

7 Peers; does as well as (6)

8 One full of vitality; one dangerous to touch (4,4)

10 Raise (7)

11 Imprisoned, locked away (7)

12 Put on clothes (5)

14 (Tsar's) edict (5)

15 "Men are – when they woo ..." (5)

19 One promising (money to charity) (7)

20 Home city of Agamemnon (7)

22 Obstinate (8)

23 Take (vehicle) at gunpoint (6)

24 With thick outsides (bread) (6)

DOWN

1 Channel port, English till 1558 (6)

2 "Damp, drizzly – in (Ishmael's) soul" (*Moby-Dick*) (8)

3 Strong; important (8)

4 Base of ship framework (4)

5 Tremble; weapon-holder (6)

6 Polish currency notes (6)

9 One rolled out for VIPs (3,6)

12 "... – when they wed" (*As You Like It*) (8)

13 Paltry, meagre (8)

16 Massage (*abbr.*) (6)

17 Polar cover (3-3)

18 Deranged fury (6)

21 Inquires, applies (for) (4)

ACROSS

1 Zambezi cascade (8,5)
8 Summarise; corral (5,2)
9 Solar System occasional visitor (5)
10 Hazelnut; a horse (3)
11 Capital of Sardinia (8)
13 Inter-state pact (6)
14 Occurring intermittently (6)
17 Liquid slopped (8)
19 Unprocessed (3)
21 Surrounded by (5)
22 Appalling action (7)
24 Rudely challenged decision (6,3,4)

DOWN

1 Ravenousness (8)
2 Fall apart; pudding (topping) (7)
3 Unusual (3)
4 Call into question (6)
5 Exact copy (9)
6 Madagascar tree-dweller (5)
7 Paving block; burrow (4)
11 Product list (9)
12 Perfect (e.g. diamond) (8)
15 A mishmash (7)
16 To caper, frolic (6)
18 Pointed end of fork (5)
20 Celebration, festival (4)
23 Fasten; equal outcome (3)

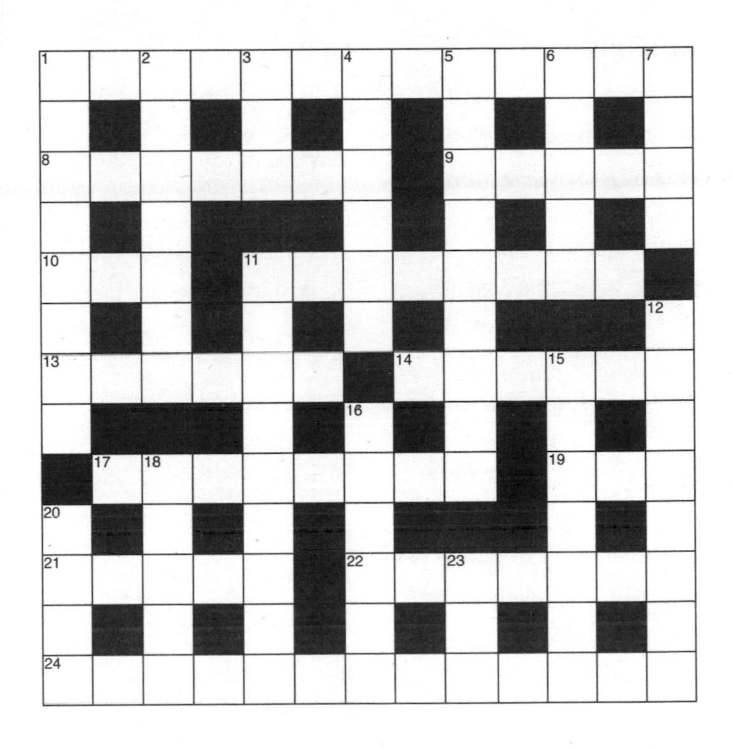

ACROSS

1 Don't tell anyone! (4,3,4)

8 "Christmas – ..." (5)

9 Louis –, bacteriologist (7)

10 "... but – ..." (4)

11 Herbert –, World War 2 Home Secretary (8)

13 Non-boarding pupil (3,3)

14 Against (another team) (6)

17 American holiday (8)

19 "... a –, ..." (4)

22 Subdivision of genus (7)

23 Light-splitting glass (5)

24 Of brilliant appearance (11)

DOWN

1 Swaggeringly masculine (5)

2 Close imitation (7)

3 Job (4)

4 Give job to (6)

5 A paper; non-participant (8)

6 Pieces for two players (5)

7 "... And when it 8 *ac*, it – ..." (6)

12 Distinguished, important people (8)

13 Contrive (6)

15 Germ-free (7)

16 Relic of past age (6)

18 "... good –" (5)

20 Send (money); cancel (penalty) (5)

21 Twirl round (4)

THE SOLUTIONS

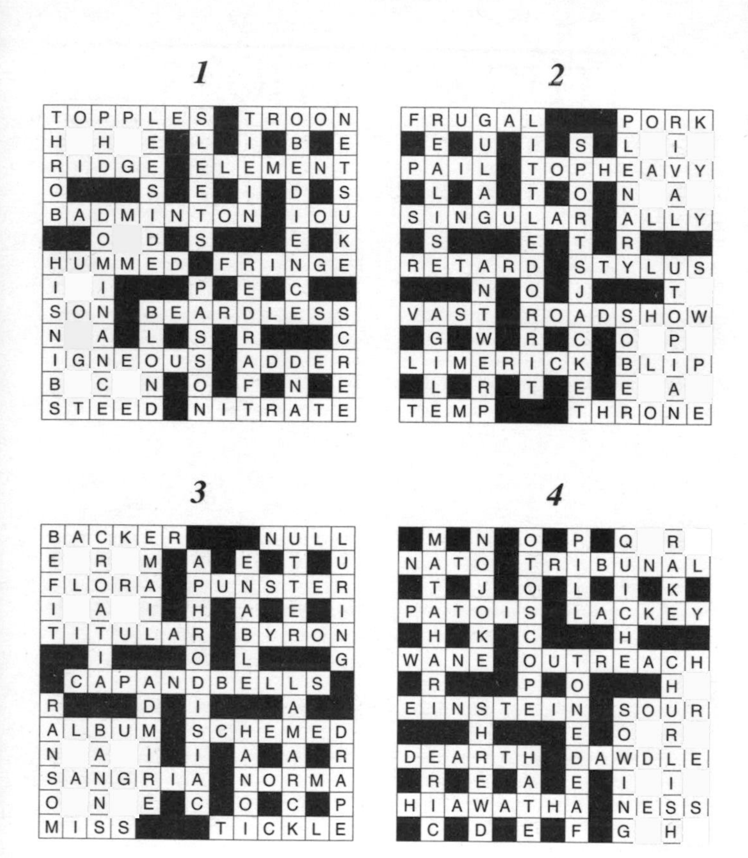
1
2
3
4

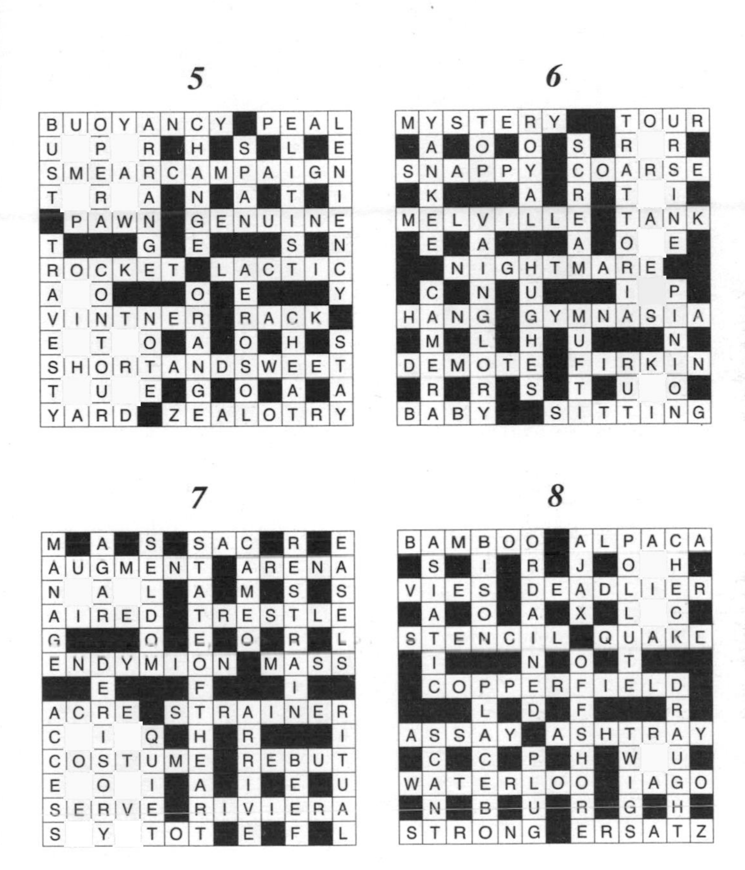
5
BUOYANCY
PEAL
SMEAR
CAMPAIGN
PAWN
GENUINE
ROCKET
LACTIC
VINTNER
RACK
SHORTANDSWEET
YARD
ZEALOTRY
6
MYSTERY
TOUR
SNAPPY
COARSE
MELVILLE
TANK
NIGHTMARE
HANG
GYMNASIA
DEMOTE
FIRKIN
BABY
SITTING
7
AUGMENT
ARENA
AIRED
TRESTLE
ENDYMION
MASS
ACRE
STRAINER
COSTUME
REBUT
SERVE
RIVIERA
TOT
8
BAMBOO
ALPACA
VIES
DEADLIER
STENCIL
QUAKE
COPPERFIELD
ASSAY
ASHTRAY
WATERLOO
IAGO
STRONG
ERSATZ

9

	B		B		H			V	A	P	I	D
	L	A	U	D	A	B	L	E		E		U
	E		S		R			N		D		R
D	A	R	T		D	E	A	D	L	I	N	E
	C		L		L			E		M		S
C	H	E	E	K	Y		O	T	H	E	R	S
		P		I				T		N		
B	L	I	N	D	S		M	A	S	T	E	R
U		C		G			A		I		N	
D	O	U	B	L	I	N	G		G	I	V	E
G		R		O			P		N		I	
E		E		V	A	L	I	D	A	T	E	
T	A	S	T	E			E		L		D	

10

Y	E	A	T	S		C			A		B	
A		L		P		H	E	A	D	W	A	Y
C	A	L	O	R	I	E			R		T	
H		U		E		F	R	A	I	L	T	Y
T	H	R	O	A	T		O		F		E	
		E		D	E	S	U	L	T	O	R	Y
	B				N		S				Y	
Q	U	A	D	R	U	P	E	D		V		
	T		R		R		D	A	N	I	E	L
S	T	R	I	P	E	S		P		O		U
	E		V			P	O	P	U	L	A	R
F	R	E	E	S	I	A		E		I		C
	Y		R			R		R	A	N	C	H

11

D	A	S	H		W	O	O	D	P	U	L	P
	B		E		E		I		R		A	
D	O	O	R	B	E	L	L		I	O	T	A
	D		O		D		F		C		T	
N	E	V	I	S		F	I	D	E	L	I	O
E			S		P		E				C	
T	R	E	M	O	R		L	A	N	D	E	D
	E				I		D		E			O
P	L	Y	W	O	O	D		H	O	U	S	E
	I		H		R		B		N		I	
J	A	N	E		E	M	E	R	A	L	D	S
	N		R		S		N		T		L	
S	T	R	E	S	S	E	D		E	Y	E	D

12

B	O	S	W	O	R	T	H			B		A
O		N		X		H		F	I	E	L	D
W	H	O	L	E	M	E	A	L		A		A
E		W		N		O		U		S	U	M
R	I	C	H		A	R	D	E	N	T		A
		A		P		Y		N				N
P	O	P	L	A	R		S	C	U	L	P	T
I				N		B		Y		U		
R		C	H	A	I	R	S		A	M	E	N
A	D	O		C		U		S		B		A
N		U		H	U	N	C	H	B	A	C	K
H	O	R	S	E		E		A		G		E
A		T			R	I	C	H	M	O	N	D

13

D	O	S	S	I	E	R			S	W	I	M
O		U		N		E		B		R		A
D	U	C	A	T		B	O	U	Q	U	E	T
O		C		E		U		R		N		A
	F	U	L	L	Y	F	L	E	D	G	E	D
		M		L		F		A				O
H	O	B	B	E	S		B	U	F	F	E	R
I				C		R		C		A		
D	O	W	N	T	H	E	D	R	A	I	N	
E		A		U		N		A		E		N
O	F	F	H	A	N	D		T	O	N	D	O
U		E		L		E		I		C		S
S	U	R	F			R	O	C	K	E	R	Y

14

C	O	L	U	M	B	U	S		S	A	I	L
A		E		A		L		J		M		E
M	A	G	I	C	A	L		O	C	E	A	N
P		A		B		A		I		R		I
	B	L	U	E		G	E	N	T	I	A	N
M				T		E				C		I
A	P	A	T	H	Y		H	A	R	A	S	S
D		L				E		C				T
R	O	U	N	D	E	D		T	O	F	F	
I		M		E		I		U		I		L
G	E	N	O	A		B	R	A	I	L	L	E
A		U		L		L		R		L		A
L	A	S	T		D	E	W	Y	E	Y	E	D

15

S	T	A	M	P	E	D	E		D	E	E	P
T		U		A		I				P		R
U	P	R	I	S	I	N	G		P	I	K	E
B		A		S		G		W		T		S
B	U	L	G	E		H	E	I	N	O	U	S
L				D		Y		D		M		
E	X	C	E	P	T		M	O	L	E	S	T
		A		A		P		W				E
G	A	N	G	W	A	Y		S	I	M	O	N
R		D		N		T		M		E		D
A	M	O	K		S	H	R	I	L	L	E	R
S		U				O		T		O		I
P	A	R	E		I	N	F	E	R	N	A	L

16

		B	A	B	Y	B	O	O	M	E	R	
A		U		L		A		L		R		
P	O	R	T	I	O	N		D	O	O	M	S
O		K		S		A		H		S		N
T	R	E	A	S	O	N		A	R	I	S	E
H						A		N		O		A
E	F	F	E	T	E		G	D	A	N	S	K
O		L		A		W						T
S	P	O	O	F		I	M	P	E	A	C	H
I		R		F		L		A		N		I
S	P	I	K	E		F	A	T	I	G	U	E
		D		T		U		I		L		F
	Z	A	B	A	G	L	I	O	N	E		

17

W	I	T	H	O	U	T	F	A	I	L		
I		W		V		R		V		U		
S	L	I	D	E		E	G	O	T	R	I	P
H		S		R		N		N		K		O
I	N	T	I	M	A	C	Y		G	I	L	L
N				U		H		T		N		Y
G	L	A	N	C	E		B	O	N	G	O	S
W		N		H		G		P				T
E	A	C	H		Q	U	A	N	D	A	R	Y
L		I		H		R		O		L		R
L	I	E	B	A	C	K		T	I	T	L	E
		N		L		H		C		A		N
		T	R	O	J	A	N	H	O	R	S	E

18

19

P		R		O		D	I	G		A		L
R	O	U	T	I	N	E		H	A	L	V	E
O		N		L		A		O		T		N
V	O	T	E	R		D	I	S	T	E	N	D
E				I		R		T		R		E
D	I	S	A	G	R	E	E		W	E	I	R
		T				C				G		
L	A	R	K		O	K	L	A	H	O	M	A
A		E		S		O		I				L
C	H	A	S	T	E	N		D	E	M	O	B
U		M		E		I		I		A		I
N	I	E	C	E		N	O	N	A	G	O	N
A		R		P	E	G		G		I		O

20

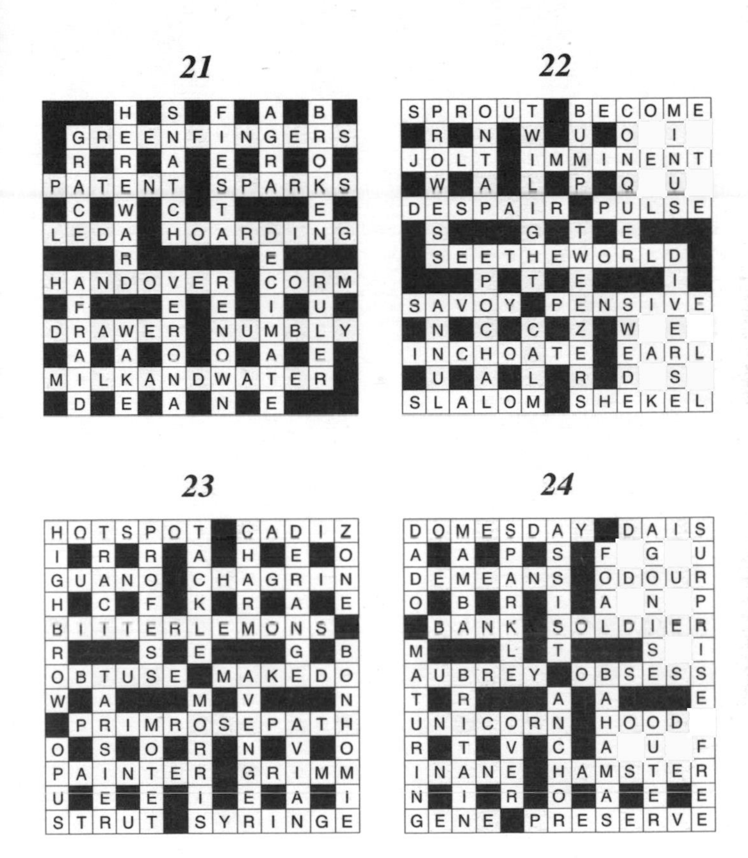

25

S	C	H	U	B	E	R	T		W	O	L	F
T		U		L		U		T		A		L
R	O	N	D	O		N	E	R	I	S	S	A
I		D		K		A		E		I		U
F	O	R	F	E	I	T		B	A	S	I	N
E		E				I		L				T
		D	E	R	I	G	U	E	U	R		
H				U		H				I		E
A	T	H	O	S		T	R	A	N	S	O	M
W		E		T		S		R		I		B
S	L	A	V	I	S	H		G	O	B	B	O
E		V		C		I		O		L		S
R	E	E	L		O	P	E	N	N	E	S	S

26

B	A	R	B	E	D				P	U	M	P
	N		O		I		S		O		O	
H	O	A	X		S	O	P	H	I	S	T	S
	M		E		A		A		N		I	
L	A	B	R	A	D	O	R		T	U	F	T
	L				V		E		E			
M	Y	O	P	I	A		S	P	R	U	C	E
			A		N		T				R	
S	L	O	T		T	A	H	I	T	I	A	N
	A		R		A		E		O		N	
S	P	R	I	N	G	E	R		T	A	M	E
	S		O		E		O		E		E	
J	E	S	T				D	E	M	U	R	E

27

28

29

30

31

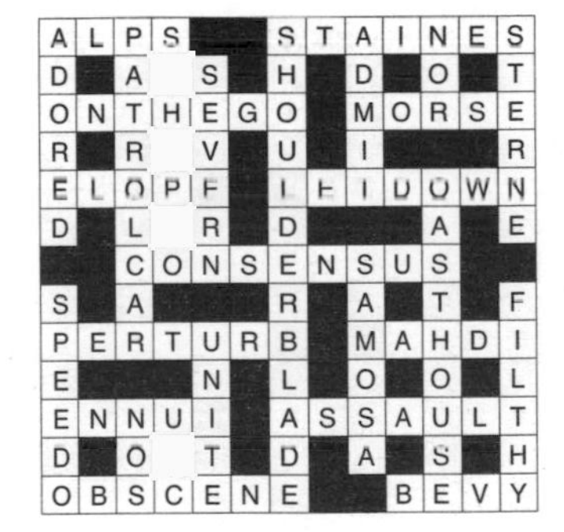

32

33

34

D	I	S	S	E	M	B	L	E		F	O	P
O		E		A		Y		P		A		U
C	O	V	E	R		S	C	H	O	L	A	R
K		E				S		E		S		I
	C	R	O	U	C	H		S	P	E	L	T
		A		N		E		I				A
D	E	L	A	N	O		B	A	T	M	A	N
I				O		C		N		I		
S	I	G	H	T		I	N	S	U	L	T	
U		L		I		T				H		L
S	P	E	N	C	E	R		P	H	O	T	O
E		B		E		U		I		U		R
D	I	E		D	I	S	P	E	N	S	E	D

35

36

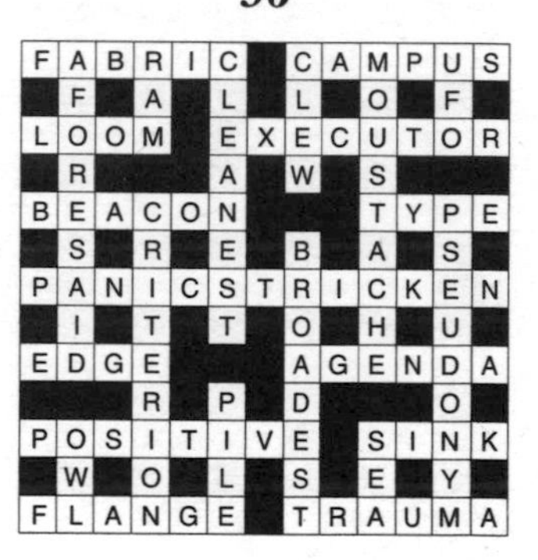

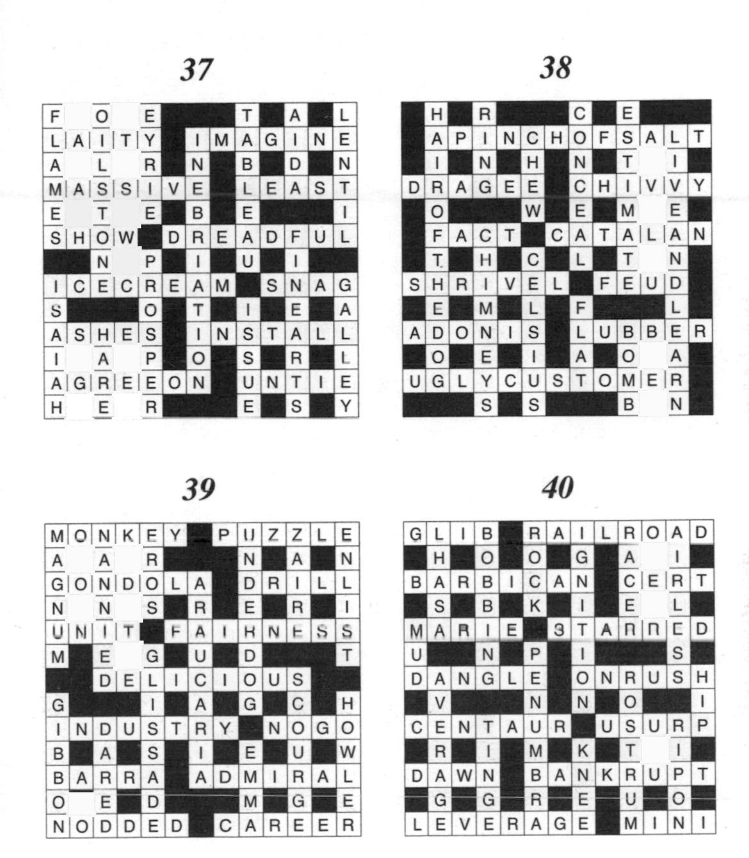
37
38
39
40

41

I		Q		B		A		S		H		M
N	E	U	T	R	A	L		P	H	A	S	E
F		I		E		M		I		W		R
O	D	D	M	A	N	O	U	T		A	W	L
R				S		S		A		I		I
M	O	U	L	T		T	E	N	S	I	O	N
		N		B				D		A		
D	I	C	K	E	N	S		P	A	N	T	S
I		L		A		U		O				T
R	O	E		T	I	T	I	L	L	A	T	E
E		S		I		U		I		T		A
C	H	A	I	N		R	E	S	P	O	N	D
T		M		G		E		H		M		Y

42

S	I	L	E	N	C	E			H	U	G	E
	C		F		A		W		A		R	
P	I	S	T	O	L		R	U	M	O	U	R
	C				V		I		F		M	
F	L	A	U	B	E	R	T		I	S	P	Y
	E		L				H		S		Y	
		E	T	I	Q	U	E	T	T	E		
	C		I		U				E		G	
P	A	L	M		A	R	C	A	D	I	A	N
	N		A		R		A				Z	
P	A	S	T	I	T		T	A	P	P	E	T
	P		U		Z		C		A		B	
G	E	R	M			S	H	A	L	L	O	W

43

B	U	C	K		U	B	I	Q	U	I	T	Y
Y		U				O		U		N		A
P	Y	R	A	M	I	D		I	N	C	U	R
A		I		A		I		C		I		N
S	P	O	N	G	E	C	A	K	E	S		
S				N		E		S		E		T
E	L	I	X	I	R		K	I	N	D	L	E
D		N		F		A		L				L
		J	O	I	E	D	E	V	I	V	R	E
O		U		C		A		E		O		T
F	U	R	Z	E		G	A	R	N	I	S	H
F		E		N		I				C		O
A	U	D	I	T	I	O	N		S	E	W	N

44

B	I	G	G	A	M	E			P	E	E	L
A		R		N		X		T		X		O
S	W	A	I	N		C	L	O	Y	I	N	G
K		P		E		E		T		S		I
	E	N	T	H	U	S	I	A	S	T	I	C
		E		A		S		L				A
P	A	L	A	T	E		W	E	A	S	E	L
O				H		C		C		T		
S	Q	U	E	A	K	Y	C	L	E	A	N	
T		S		W		G		I		M		U
B	A	H	R	A	I	N		P	R	I	N	T
A		E		Y		E		S		N		A
G	U	R	U			T	H	E	W	A	S	H

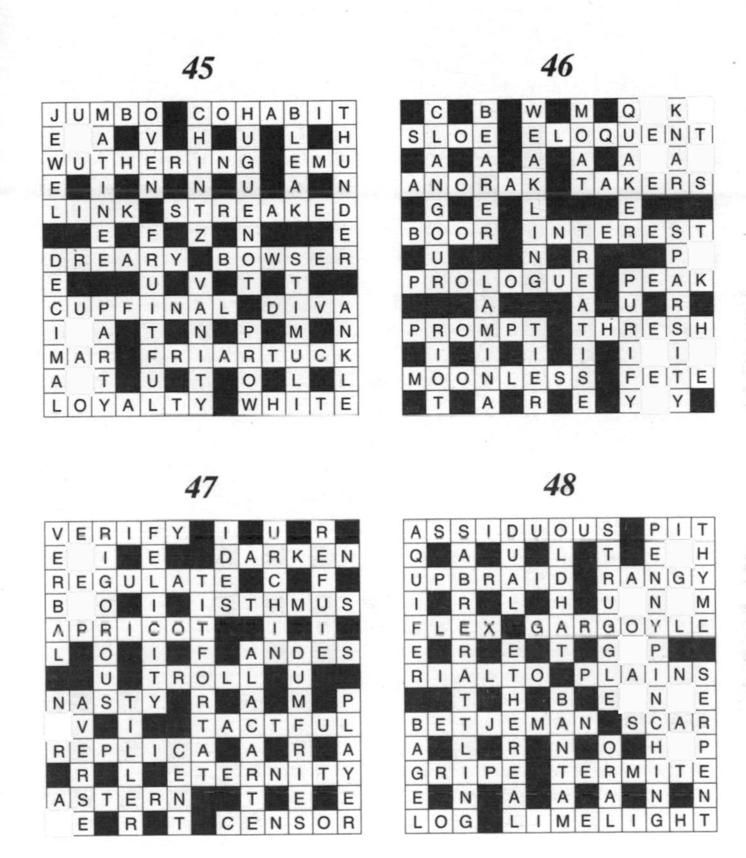
45
46
47
48

49

R	H	A	P	S	O	D	Y	■	R	E	A	D
O		B		K	■	R	■	B	■	X	■	O
T	R	I	N	I	T	Y	■	A	P	I	N	G
A		D		P	■	I	■	L	■	G	■	G
	L	E	A	P	■	C	O	L	L	E	G	E
C	■	■	■	E	■	E	■	■	■	N	■	R
O	X	F	O	R	D	■	K	E	T	T	L	E
N		A	■	■	■	T	■	X	■	■	■	L
F	O	U	N	D	E	R	■	P	O	P	E	■
U		V		U	■	I	■	L	■	E	■	M
S	T	I	C	K	■	V	I	O	L	A	T	E
E		S		E	■	I	■	D	■	C	■	L
D	A	M	P	■	S	A	F	E	S	E	A	T

50

G	O	B	L	E	T	■	S	C	O	R	E	R
O	■	E	■	■	U	■	■	R	■	I	■	E
B	O	L	E	■	T	R	O	U	B	L	E	D
L	■	I	■	■	O	■	■	D	■	E	■	U
I	N	T	E	G	R	A	T	E	■	■	■	C
N	■	T	■	E	■	L	■	N	I	C	H	E
■	■	L	■	S	L	I	C	E	■	A	■	■
C	H	E	S	T	■	K	■	S	■	R	■	S
U	■	■	■	A	Y	E	R	S	R	O	C	K
S	■	F	■	T	■	■	I	■	■	L	■	I
T	E	R	M	I	N	U	S	■	D	I	A	L
E	■	E	■	O	■	■	E	■	■	N	■	L
R	O	T	U	N	D	■	R	E	M	E	D	Y

51

C	O	W	L	I	N	G	■	R	A	D	A	R
A		O		N	■	R	■	O	■	E	■	A
S	H	E	A	F	■	E	N	D	E	M	I	C
T	■	■	■	E	■	T	■	E	■	E	■	K
E	S	P	E	R	A	N	T	O	■	A	X	E
■	■	E		N	■	A	■	■	■	N	■	T
P	A	R	S	O	N	■	A	P	R	O	N	S
E		S	■	■	■	G	■	R	■	U	■	■
L	E	O	■	E	N	A	M	O	U	R	E	D
I		N	■	V	■	R	■	F	■	■	■	O
S	T	A	T	I	O	N	■	A	R	R	O	W
S		T		C	■	E	■	N	■	U	■	S
E	X	E	R	T	■	T	R	E	M	B	L	E

52

M	A	N	Y	■	■	G	R	A	P	H	I	C
U	■	E	■	T	■	E	■	B	■	O	■	O
S	A	W	D	U	S	T	■	H	A	P	P	Y
C	■	M	■	N	■	T	■	O	■	■	■	O
L	E	A	R	N	■	H	A	R	I	C	O	T
E	■	R	■	E	■	E	■	■	■	R	■	E
■	■	K	I	L	O	M	E	T	R	E	■	■
P	■	E	■	■	■	E	■	A	■	S	■	S
R	E	T	U	R	N	S	■	C	A	C	H	E
O	■	■	■	A	■	S	■	T	■	E	■	A
F	A	M	E	D	■	A	V	I	G	N	O	N
I	■	O	■	O	■	G	■	C	■	D	■	C
T	R	A	I	N	E	E	■	■	T	O	M	E

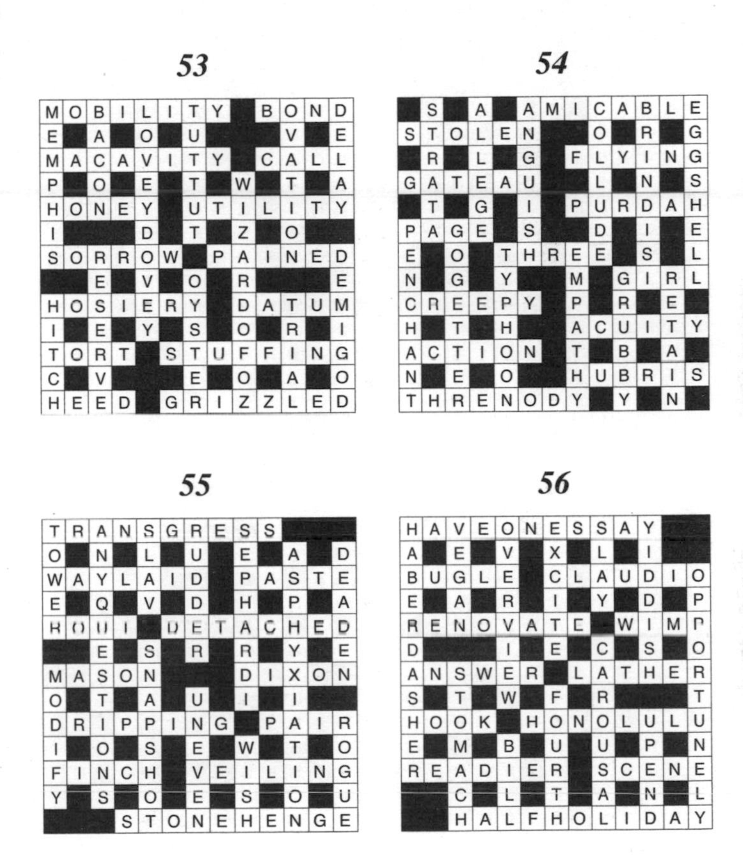
53
54
55
56

57

C	A	V	I	L	■	V	■	■	M	■	B	■
U		O		A	■	E	T	H	I	C	A	L
P	A	R	Q	U	E	T	■	■	R	■	L	■
I		T		N	■	O	V	E	R	A	C	T
D	R	E	N	C	H	■	I	■	O	■	O	■
■	■	X	■	H	A	N	K	E	R	I	N	G
■	P	■	■	■	Z	■	I	■	■	■	Y	■
J	O	H	N	W	A	Y	N	E	■	A	■	■
■	T		O	■	R	■	G	U	F	F	A	W
F	O	R	B	I	D	S	■	L	■	F	■	H
	M		O	■	■	I	S	O	T	O	P	E
H	A	N	D	B	A	G	■	G	■	R	■	E
■	C		Y	■	■	H	■	Y	O	D	E	L

58

B	R	O	O	K	I	N	G	■	H	I	L	L
U	■	C	■	E	■	I	■	■	■	N	■	U
M	O	T	T	E	■	P	U	S	H	K	I	N
B	■	E	■	P	■	P	■	T	■	L	■	G
L	O	T	■	A	B	O	R	I	G	I	N	E
E	■	■	■	N	■	N	■	G	■	N	■	■
D	U	B	B	E	D	■	E	M	I	G	R	E
■	■	L	■	Y	■	N	■	A	■	■	■	M
S	C	A	P	E	G	O	A	T	■	P	U	B
W	■	N	■	O	■	V	■	I	■	L	■	R
A	S	K	A	N	C	E	■	S	C	U	B	A
R	■	E	■	■	■	N	■	E	■	T	■	C
M	O	T	E	■	H	A	N	D	S	O	M	E

59

P	I	P	E	■	F	I	R	S	T	A	I	D
E		A		B	■	M	■	C	■	B	■	I
M	I	S	E	R	■	P	U	R	P	O	S	E
B		S		A	■	O	■	U	■	V	■	T
R	O	I	S	T	E	R	■	P	R	E	Y	■
O		O	■	■	■	T	■	L	■	R	■	C
K	I	N	D	L	Y	■	C	E	R	E	A	L
E		S		A	■	C	■	■	■	P	■	I
■	D	U	N	E	■	H	O	M	E	R	U	N
B		N		R	■	I	■	U	■	O	■	C
U	P	D	A	T	E	S	■	S	M	A	S	H
L		A		E	■	E	■	T	■	C	■	E
B	O	Y	I	S	H	L	Y	■	T	H	O	R

60

■	S	■	Z	■	L	■	■	A	U	G	U	R
■	Q	U	I	X	O	T	I	C	■	A	■	E
■	U	■	T	■	W	■	■	T	■	D	■	J
F	I	S	H	■	K	A	M	I	K	A	Z	E
■	N	■	E	■	E	■	■	V	■	B	■	C
S	T	U	R	D	Y	■	M	A	H	O	U	T
■	■	N	■	O	■	■	■	T	■	U	■	■
S	Q	U	A	W	K	■	V	E	R	T	E	X
A	■	S	■	N	■	■	I	■	A	■	Q	■
T	R	A	N	S	F	E	R	■	P	O	U	T
R	■	B	■	I	■	■	G	■	T	■	I	■
A	■	L	■	D	E	M	I	J	O	H	N	■
P	A	Y	E	E	■	■	L	■	R	■	E	■

61

F	E	C	K	L	E	S	S	■	■	S	■	D
A	■	A		A	■	I	■	B	A	T	H	E
C	O	M	M	I	T	T	A	L	■	A	■	P
E	■	P	■	R	■	T	■	O	■	K	I	R
T	R	I	M		R	E	M	O	V	E	■	E
■	■	O		B	■	R	■	M	■	■	■	S
L	O	N	E	L	Y	■	H	E	A	R	T	S
E	■	■	■	A	■	M	■	R	■	E	■	■
A	■	B	A	T	T	E	R	■	S	T	A	B
F	I	R	■	A	■	A	■	K	■	R	■	A
L	■	A	■	N	E	G	L	I	G	E	N	T
E	L	I	O	T	■	R	■	N	■	A	■	O
T	■	D	■	■	H	E	I	G	H	T	E	N

62

H	A	T	C	H	E	T	■	■	B	L	U	R
O	■	R	■	A	■	A	■	Q		A	■	O
C	L	A	I	M	■	V	A	U	N	T	E	D
K	■	G	■	P	■	E	■	A		I	■	G
■	H	E	S	T	E	R	P	R	Y	N	N	E
■	■	D	■	O	■	N	■	T	■	■	■	R
S	A	Y	I	N	G	■	C	E	N	S	U	S
E	■	■	■	C	■	A	■	R		P	■	■
S	C	H	O	O	L	M	A	S	T	E	R	■
S	■	A	■	U	■	O	■	T		C	■	I
I	N	V	E	R	S	E	■	A	L	I	G	N
O	■	E	■	T	■	B	■	F		A	■	C
N	I	N	E	■	■	A	L	F	A	L	F	A

63

H	I	D	E	■	S	P	E	C	I	M	E	N
U	■	I	■	■	■	H	■	A	■	I	■	E
S	I	D	E	■	F	O	R	M	U	L	A	E
H	■	A		O	■	T	■	O	■	L	■	P
H	O	C	U	S	P	O	C	U	S	■	■	■
U	■	T		C	■	N	■	F	■	P	■	L
S	P	I	R	I	T	■	P	L	E	A	S	E
H	■	C		L	■	D	■	A	■	N	■	C
■	■	■	F	L	Y	I	N	G	B	O	A	T
F	■	S		A	■	F	■	E	■	R	■	U
I	D	E	N	T	I	F	Y	■	F	A	I	R
L	■	E	■	E	■	E	■	■	■	M	■	E
L	A	P	I	D	A	R	Y	■	H	A	I	R

64

■	S	C	H	O	L	A	S	T	I	C	■	■
■	■	A	■	N	■	D	■	R		E	■	W
P	U	R	S	U	E	R	■	O	U	N	C	E
I	■	G	■	S	■	O	■	P		T	■	I
C	O	O	P	■	D	I	V	I	D	I	N	G
K	■	■	■	D	■	T	■	C		M	■	H
P	U	M	M	E	L	■	L	A	T	E	N	T
O	■	R	■	L	■	C	■	L	■	■	■	L
C	A	R	N	I	V	A	L	■	F	I	L	E
K	■	I	■	V	■	R	■	Y		G	■	S
E	A	G	L	E	■	T	R	O	I	L	U	S
T	■	H	■	R	■	O	■	G	■	O	■	■
■	■	T	R	Y	I	N	G	I	T	O	N	■

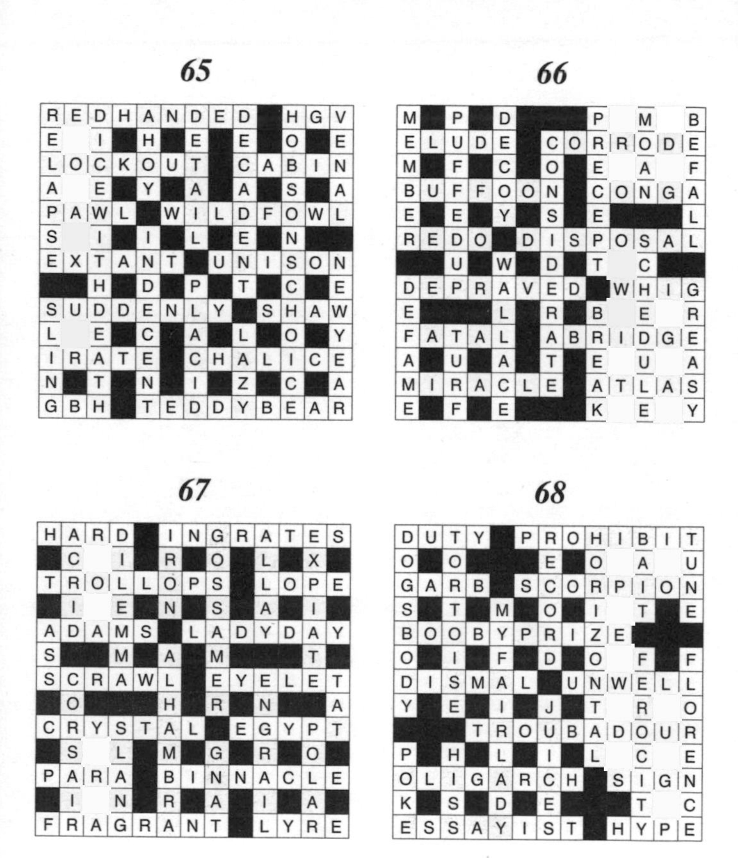
65
REDHANDED HGV
E I H E E O E
LOCKOUT CABIN
A E Y A A S A
PAWL WILDFOWL
S I I L E N
EXTANT UNISON
H D P T C E
SUDDENLY SHAW
L E C A L O Y
IRATE CHALICE
N T N I Z C A
GBH TEDDYBEAR
66
M P D P M B
ELUDE CORRODE
M F C O E A F
BUFFOON CONGA
E E Y S E L
REDO DISPOSAL
U W D T C
DEPRAVED WHIG
E L R B E R
FATAL ABRIDGE
A U A T E U A
MIRACLE ATLAS
E F E K E Y
67
HARD INGRATES
C I R O L X
TROLLOPS LOPE
I E N S A I
ADAMS LADYDAY
S M A M T
SCRAWL EYELET
O H R N A
CRYSTAL EGYPT
S L M G R O
PARA BINNACLE
I N R A I A
FRAGRANT LYRE
68
DUTY PROHIBIT
O O E O A U
GARB SCORPION
S T M O I T E
BOOBYPRIZE
O I F D O F F
DISMAL UNWELL
Y E I J T R O
TROUBADOUR
P H L I L C E
OLIGARCH SIGN
K S D E T C
ESSAYIST HYPE

69

D	R	A	S	T	I	C		G	A	V	E	L
O		C		E		O		U		I		E
D	R	O	L	L		U	L	Y	A	N	O	V
G		R		L		R		S		E		E
S	A	N	C	T	I	T	Y		A	G	U	E
O				A		E		W		A		
N	O	H	O	L	D	S	B	A	R	R	E	D
		A		E		Y		R				Y
R	A	N	T		S	T	R	I	C	K	E	N
E		G		B		I		N		O		A
C	O	M	M	E	N	T		E	V	A	N	S
A		A		L		L		S		L		T
P	A	N	E	L		E	C	S	T	A	S	Y

70

	C		H				T		B			
	H	A	I	R	S	B	R	E	A	D	T	H
	R		L		U		A		S		H	
L	I	N	T	E	L		F	A	T	C	A	T
	S				K		F		I		T	
	T	I	L	E		W	I	L	L	O	W	Y
	M		A		F		C		L		O	
G	A	I	N	S	A	Y		H	E	W	N	
	S		D		N		L				T	
H	E	R	M	I	T		O	T	T	A	W	A
	V		A		A		S		H		A	
W	E	I	R	D	S	I	S	T	E	R	S	
			K		Y				M		H	

71

	P				S	E	N	S	I	B	L	E
S	A	V	A	N	T			Q		I		X
	R		M		A		S	U	B	T	L	E
C	A	B	B	A	G	E		A		E		M
	P		I		N			S	C	R	A	P
W	E	S	T	W	A	R	D	H	O			T
	T		I		T		I		N		I	
C			O	P	E	N	S	E	S	A	M	E
R	H	I	N	E			G		T		P	
E		M		N		L	U	N	A	T	I	C
C	L	A	Q	U	E		I		N		O	
H		G		R			S	E	T	O	U	T
E	V	E	R	Y	O	N	E				S	

72

A	S	C	O	T		L	I	M	I	T	E	D
B		O		U		I		A		U		O
E	N	N	O	B	L	E		E	X	T	O	L
R		T		B		L		S		T		E
D	I	A	R	Y		O	B	T	A	I	N	
E		C				W		R				H
E	I	T	H	E	R		S	O	O	T	H	E
N				A		S				W		A
	Q	U	A	R	R	Y		F	L	I	N	T
S		N		N		D		I		S		E
L	O	D	G	E		N	E	G	A	T	E	D
U		U		S		E		H		E		L
R	E	E	N	T	R	Y		T	A	R	D	Y

73

T	R	E	S	P	A	S	S		F	U	S	E
R			W		D		E		E		E	
A		S	A	L	V	O	L	A	T	I	L	E
P	I	T	Y		E		L		T		E	
P		O			R		S		L		C	
I	N	D	E	N	T		O	M	E	R	T	A
S		G			I	N	N			I		L
T	H	E	B	E	S		E	X	O	D	U	S
	O		U		E		S			D		A
	N		R		M		S		S	L	I	T
T	O	U	R	D	E	F	O	R	C	E		I
	U		O		N		U		U			A
C	R	O	W		T	A	L	K	D	O	W	N

74

	A		R		M		A		D		A	
T	R	U	E		A	P	P	R	O	A	C	H
	M		F		N		S		U		H	
F	E	C	U	N	D		E	M	B	L	E	M
	N		S		A				L			
V	I	L	E		R	E	C	R	E	A	T	E
	A				I		H				I	
I	N	F	R	I	N	G	E		D	U	C	K
			A				C		I		K	
T	U	N	D	R	A		K	E	E	N	L	Y
	L		I		K		I		P		I	
I	N	F	U	S	I	O	N		P	O	S	T
	A		M		N		G		E		H	

75

W	I	L	L	I	A	M		S	T	A	N	D
E		O		G		O		A		L		I
B	R	O	W	N		D	O	U	G	L	A	S
E				O		E		C		O		A
R	A	S	P	B	E	R	R	Y		W	E	B
		A		L		N				A		L
G	I	N	G	E	R		J	U	M	B	L	E
O		H				V		P		L		
L	E	E		P	R	O	P	R	I	E	T	Y
I		D		I		O		I				O
A	E	R	A	T	E	D		G	R	A	I	N
T		I		H		O		H		G		K
H	E	N	R	Y		O	U	T	L	A	W	S

76

N	E	P	O	T	I	S	M		C	A	L	F
O		L		H		W		M		L		E
T	R	U	C	E		E	V	I	D	E	N	T
A		M		T		E		D		R		I
R	E	M	N	A	N	T		G	O	T	H	S
Y		E				N		E				H
		T	H	I	N	O	N	T	O	P		
C				R		T				R		S
A	G	G	R	O		H	O	L	D	O	U	T
N		R		N		I		I		V		A
C	A	U	T	I	O	N		S	H	E	E	N
A		E		C		G		L		R		C
N	I	L	E		A	S	S	E	M	B	L	E

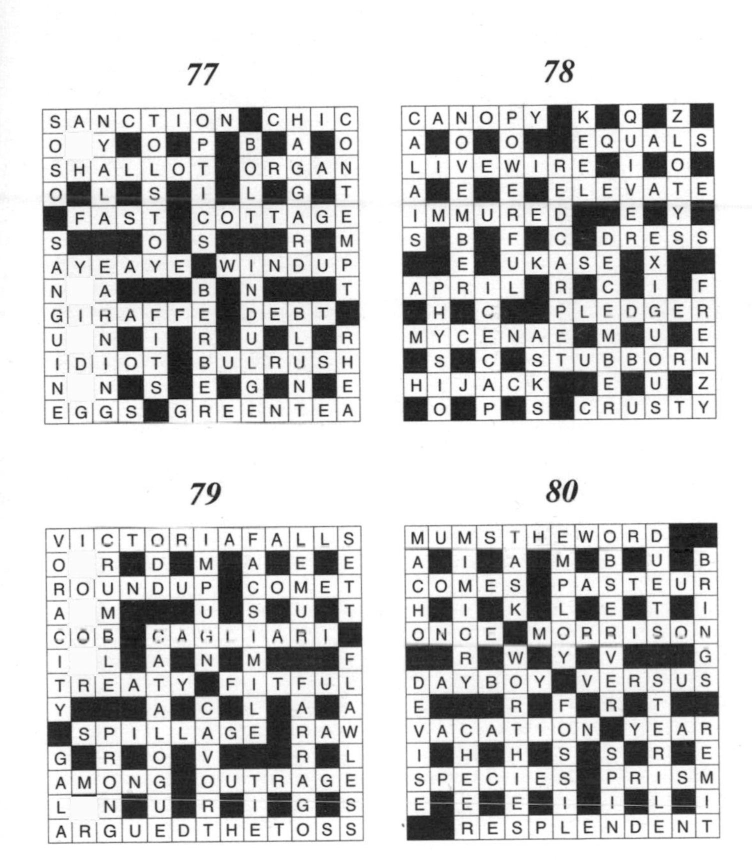
77
78
79
80

NOTES

NOTES

NOTES

NOTES